Visual
human biology

G. D. Chalk
G. P. J. Baster

Edward Arnold

© G.D. Chalk and
G.P.J. Baster 1976
First published 1976
by Edward Arnold (Publishers) Ltd
25 Hill Street London W1X 8LL
Reprinted 1978
ISBN: 0 7131 0014 1

Designed and illustrated by D.P. Press, Sevenoaks,
Kent.
Printed in Great Britain by The Pitman Press, Bath.

Contents

This book is designed to be read in the order written.
For reference the main sections are as follows:

Acknowledgements

We are indebted to many colleagues at Barking
College of Technology for helpful suggestions and
comments on the contents of this book and to
generations of patient students who by their under-
standing (or lack of it) have helped us evolve the
notes and diagrams we have used. We would like to
thank Stella Robinson of D.P. Press Ltd., for her
assistance in researching the diagrams. We also wish
to acknowledge the following sources of photographs
and drawings:
The British Museum (Natural History) for all photographs on page 3; The Wellcome Museum of Medical
Science for all photographs on pages 54, 56, 57 and
74; The Wellcome Research Institute for the photograph on page 84; Guy's Hospital Medical School for
both photographs on page 70; Oldchurch Hospital,
Romford for the Mongol Karyotype on page 84;
Mr H. Gove and the Essex Water Company for the
photograph of a filter bed under construction on
page 113; The London Hospital for the photograph
on page 131.

We are grateful to the St. John Ambulance Association
and Brigade, St. Andrew's Ambulance Association and
the British Red Cross Society for permission to use
drawings illustrating resuscitation and cardiac massage
in the First Aid section. It is recommended that the
reader attends first aid sessions run by these
Associations.

G.D. Chalk
G.P. Baster

The publishers would like to thank the following
for providing photographs:
Lucas Aerospace Ltd (page 129), Draeger Medical Ltd
(page 130), Sheelah Latham (page 132), and Hewlett
Packard (page 133).

Preface

The process of learning involves the student in juggling mental pictures, associating them in a logical manner and then storing them away for future recall. The annotated diagrams in this book are presented in a logical sequence and should be studied rather than merely looked at. Constant associations should be made with adjacent drawings and the functions of the parts within the body as a whole.

This book is primarily intended for use by students of G.C.E. Ordinary Level Human Biology or C.S.E. mode III courses. It should also be invaluable for Pre-nursing or Medical and Welfare students. Because these syllabuses are covered, the reader should make sure that all parts of the book are relevant to his own course of study by referring to his own curriculum. We have tried to cover all G.C.E. syllabuses and the extra section on first aid should be of use to all readers. Medical machines are widely used in nursing so explanations are given of how the commonest ones function.

Most modern examination papers are based on multiple-choice and fixed-response questions, often including photographs or diagrams about which questions are asked. This new type of textbook should be invaluable for answering these questions. Examples of the type of questions asked are included so that the reader can familiarise himself with them.

Teachers should find this book useful as it will mean fewer diagrams have to be drawn on boards and projectors. It will be especially useful if there are students present with a limited grasp of English.

G.D. Chalk
G.P. Baster

Man the animal

Mammals

Like other mammals (for example mice, dogs, cows and horses) man has hair on his body, has a constant temperature above that of his surroundings, gives birth to live young and feeds them on milk, a secretion of the mammary glands, during the early part of their lives.

The evolution of man

Man is a member of that group of mammals called the primates (order Primata). This group includes the tree shrews, lemurs, tarsiers, monkeys and apes.

All primates have evolved over millions of years from tree-living insectivores, probably similar to the tree shrew which lives today.

A tree shrew

Man, together with the monkeys, gibbons and apes, is placed by biologists in the sub-order Anthropoidea, man himself being of the family Hominidae.

This family of which, today, man is the only member, has evolved within the last million years.

Australopithecus (Southern Ape)

had both ape-like and man-like features, walked erect, was about four feet in height

Pithecanthropus

remains have been discovered in China, Java and North Africa. Were more advanced than Australopithecus, had a large brain. They made tools out of stone, hunted animals for food and had learned to use fire

Neanderthal man

was wide-spread in Europe, Asia and North Africa around 200 000 years ago. Made a wide variety of tools out of flint

Modern man

Some of Man's ancestors

1. Australopithecus

2. Pithecanthropus

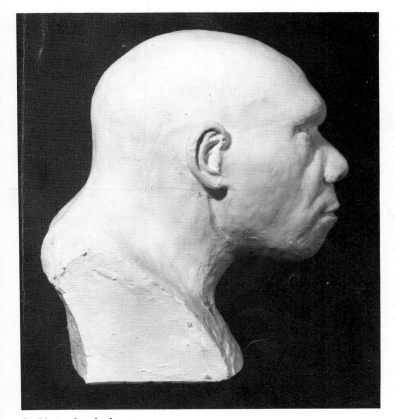

3. Neanderthal man

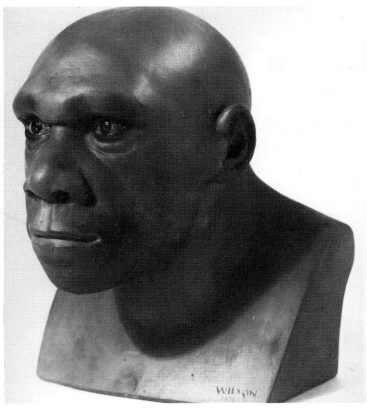

4. Cro-magnon man
The immediate ancestor of modern man, remains found in France.

Units of the body

Cells

The body of a human being is made up of millions of microscopic units known as cells.

The diagram shows a group of three human cells from the lining of the mouth. Not a great deal of detail is visible, the cytoplasm looks lumpy and is described as being granular.

With even the most powerful light microscope it is not possible to magnify an object more than 1500 times without loss of detail and so the detailed structure of the cytoplasm did not become obvious until the development of the electron microscope. With the electron microscope, magnifications of over 500 000 times can be achieved.

The material of which cells are made is called protoplasm.

The protoplasm is divided into two regions i) nucleus ii) cytoplasm.

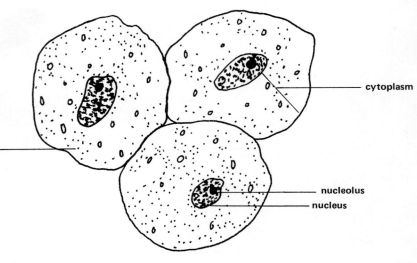

cytoplasm

nucleolus

nucleus

cytoplasm granular

The diagram below shows the complexity of the cytoplasm as shown by the electron microscope.

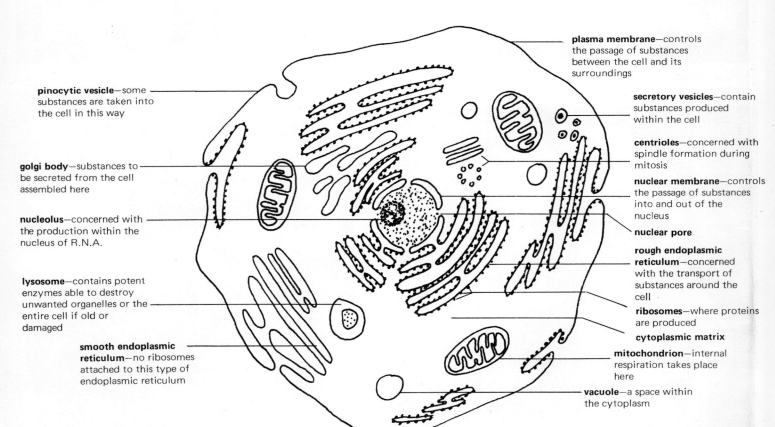

pinocytic vesicle—some substances are taken into the cell in this way

golgi body—substances to be secreted from the cell assembled here

nucleolus—concerned with the production within the nucleus of R.N.A.

lysosome—contains potent enzymes able to destroy unwanted organelles or the entire cell if old or damaged

smooth endoplasmic reticulum—no ribosomes attached to this type of endoplasmic reticulum

plasma membrane—controls the passage of substances between the cell and its surroundings

secretory vesicles—contain substances produced within the cell

centrioles—concerned with spindle formation during mitosis

nuclear membrane—controls the passage of substances into and out of the nucleus

nuclear pore

rough endoplasmic reticulum—concerned with the transport of substances around the cell

ribosomes—where proteins are produced

cytoplasmic matrix

mitochondrion—internal respiration takes place here

vacuole—a space within the cytoplasm

An organelle is the name given to a definite structure within the cell, e.g. Mitochondria, endoplasmic reticulum, lysosomes.

You will learn about the functions of some of these later.

Cells

The cells which go to make up the human body show much variation in form, shape and content. Cells become specialised to carry out particular jobs within the body. Masses of cells that are similar in appearance and function are known as tissues. The tissues of the body can be conveniently divided into four groups.

Epithelial tissues

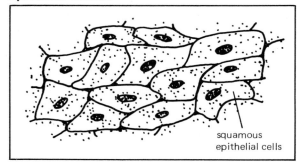

squamous
epithelial cells

These are tissues which cover both internal and external surfaces of the body. Their main function is protective. They are found in the surface of the skin when the cells are filled with a waterproof material; these cells are dead. Epithelial cells also line the mouth, the chest cavity and the abdominal cavity.

Connective tissues

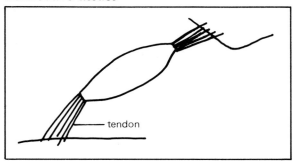

tendon

These bind together and give support to other tissues of the body. They are also found filling cavities within the body, holding bundles of muscle fibres together and forming tendons of muscles and ligaments of joints.

Muscular tissues

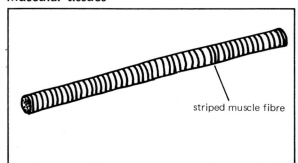

striped muscle fibre

These are contractile and are responsible for bringing about movement. These cells form the muscles of the body; there are different types of muscle cells each forming a different type of muscle.

Nervous tissues

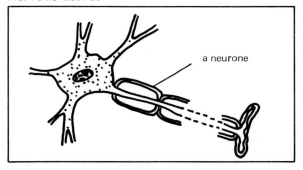

a neurone

Consist of a network of very special cells, the function of which is to transmit electrical messages. Bundles of these cells form the nerves, the spinal cord and the brain; there are different types of nerve cells, each with a different function.

Epithelial tissues

These are surfaces within the body the linings of which must be permeable to substances in solution, for example the linings of capillaries, the alveoli of the lungs and the Bowman's capsules within the kidneys. In such places, squamous epithelium is found.

Membranes
An epithelial tissue which secretes a lubricating fluid is known as a membrane. There are three kinds of membrane.

1 Synovial membranes
Found lining the interior of joints. Secrete synovial fluid.

Mucous membranes
Found lining the repiratory tract and alimentary canal. Secrete mucus.

3 Serous membranes
Found lining inner surface of abdomen and thorax, also covering surface of organs. Secretes serum.

Lining the inner surface of the alimentary canal trachea, bronchi and the oviduct is found a tissue composed of column shaped cells standing on a basement membrane. From the free surface of these cells project delicate, hair-like structures called cilia.

The cilia projecting from the tissue lining the respiratory tract beat rapidly and rhythmically causing the mucus to flow upwards towards the mouth. Particles of dust and other foreign materials become caught up in the mucus and are carried away from the lungs. In the oviduct, the ciliated epithelium is responsible for the movement of the egg towards the uterus.

Lining the inner surface of the alimentary canal are found tall, column shaped cells that are known as columnar epithelium.

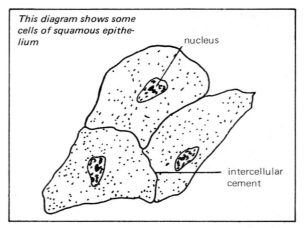

This diagram shows some cells of squamous epithelium

nucleus

intercellular cement

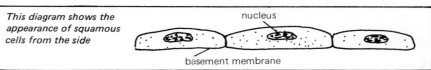

This diagram shows the appearance of squamous cells from the side

nucleus

basement membrane

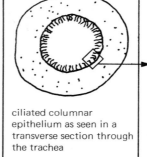

ciliated columnar epithelium as seen in a transverse section through the trachea

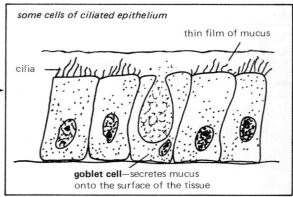

some cells of ciliated epithelium

thin film of mucus

cilia

goblet cell—secretes mucus onto the surface of the tissue

Those parts of the body that are subjected to friction, for example the outer surface of the body, the inner surface of the oesophagus, and vagina, are lined by stratified epithelium. Notice that this tissue is made up of several layers of cells. Its function is protective.

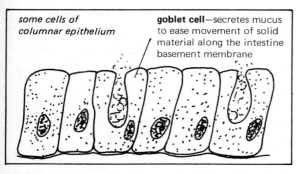

some cells of columnar epithelium

goblet cell—secretes mucus to ease movement of solid material along the intestine

basement membrane

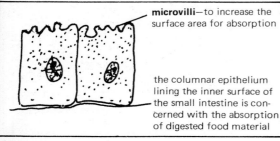

microvilli—to increase the surface area for absorption

the columnar epithelium lining the inner surface of the small intestine is concerned with the absorption of digested food material

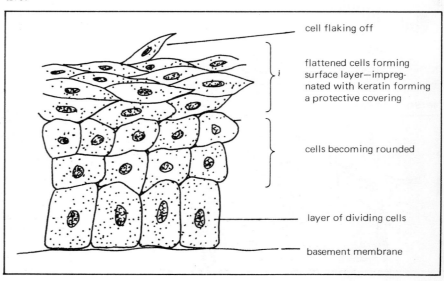

cell flaking off

flattened cells forming surface layer—impregnated with keratin forming a protective covering

cells becoming rounded

layer of dividing cells

basement membrane

Connective tissues

Found joining together other tissues and organs of
the body and giving support to more delicate tissues.

White non-elastic fibres

Very strong, do not stretch, found attaching muscles
to bones as tendons.

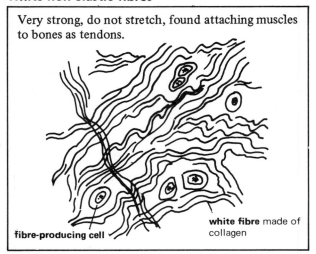

fibre-producing cell

white fibre made of
collagen

Yellow elastic fibres

These fibres do stretch. Found in wall of arteries
and veins and in lungs.

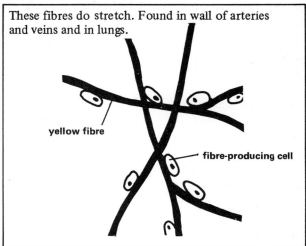

yellow fibre

fibre-producing cell

Areolar or loose connective tissue

Found beneath the skin and filling cavities within
the body.

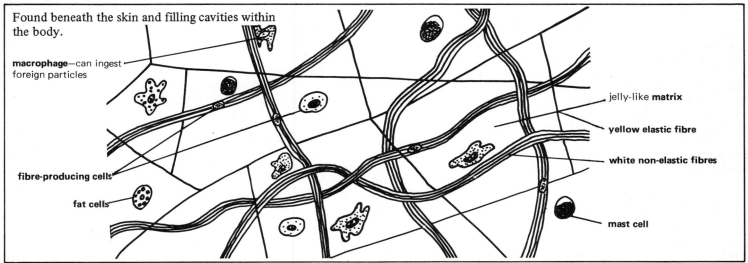

macrophage—can ingest
foreign particles

jelly-like **matrix**

yellow elastic fibre

white non-elastic fibres

fibre-producing cells

fat cells

mast cell

Cartilage

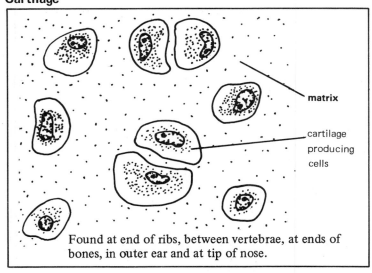

matrix

cartilage
producing
cells

Found at end of ribs, between vertebrae, at ends of
bones, in outer ear and at tip of nose.

Bone

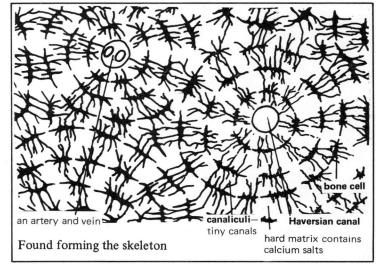

bone cell

an artery and vein

canaliculi—
tiny canals

Haversian canal

hard matrix contains
calcium salts

Found forming the skeleton

7

Muscular tissues

Responsible for bringing about movement.

There are three types of muscle:

1. Voluntary or striped muscle

Under voluntary conscious control by the brain.
Found attached to the bones of the skeleton, this
type of muscle is used in movement. Striped muscles
are capable of doing a great deal of work but will tire
easily.

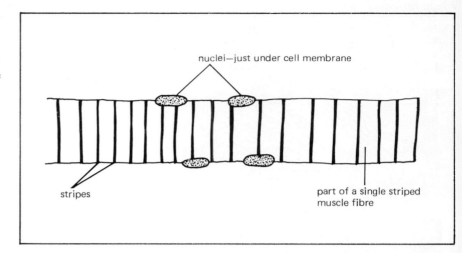

nuclei—just under cell membrane

stripes

part of a single striped
muscle fibre

2. Involuntary or unstriped muscle

Not under conscious control. Found in wall of
alimentary canal, in the wall of blood vessels and in
the uterus and bladder. These muscles cannot produce strong contractions and so are not used for
movement. They do not tire easily and are used for
continuous work.

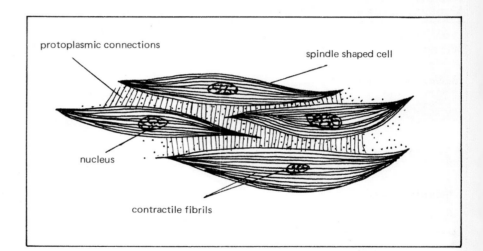

protoplasmic connections

spindle shaped cell

nucleus

contractile fibrils

3. Cardiac muscle

Found **only** in the wall of the heart. Never tires and
can produce the strong contractions needed to pump
blood around the body. This very specialised muscle
requires large supplies of oxygen.

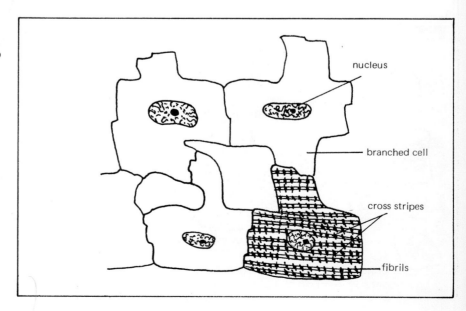

nucleus

branched cell

cross stripes

fibrils

Cell division

As we shall see later, a human being consisting of many thousands of cells, originates as a single cell called the zygote, which is formed as a result of the joining together of the male sex cell (or sperm) and the female sex cell (or ovum). This single cell divides to form two cells which themselves divide to form four cells. By repeated cell division a human being develops.

Stages in cell division

1. When a cell is not dividing the chromosomes within the nucleus are not visible. Notice that the centriole has already divided.

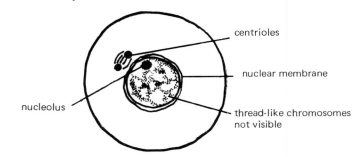

centrioles

nuclear membrane

nucleolus

thread-like chromosomes not visible

2. The two centrioles move to opposite poles of the cell.

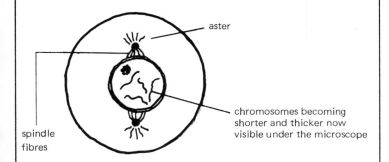

aster

spindle fibres

chromosomes becoming shorter and thicker now visible under the microscope

3. The nucleolus has now disappeared.

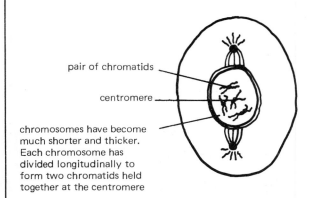

pair of chromatids

centromere

chromosomes have become much shorter and thicker. Each chromosome has divided longitudinally to form two chromatids held together at the centromere

4. The nuclear membrane has broken down. Pairs of chromatids arranged around the equator of cell attached to spindle fibres by centromeres.

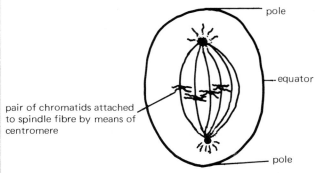

pole

equator

pair of chromatids attached to spindle fibre by means of centromere

pole

5. The centromeres have divided and the individual chromatids move towards opposite poles of the cell.

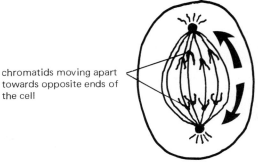

chromatids moving apart towards opposite ends of the cell

6. 7. Chromosomes in the nuclei of the two new cells become long and thread-like and invisible again.

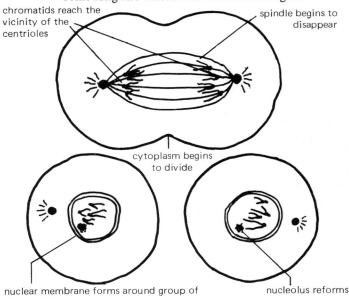

chromatids reach the vicinity of the centrioles

spindle begins to disappear

cytoplasm begins to divide

nuclear membrane forms around group of chromatids

nucleolus reforms

Note that the two new cells have the same number of chromosomes as each other and as the parent cell. They are also genetically identical.
This type of cell division is known as mitosis.
Chromosome in the nuclei of the two new cells become long and thread-like and invisible again.

Nutrition

Food

Food supplies the body with energy and it is necessary for the building up of new tissues and for the repair of damaged tissues. For full health, the diet must contain sufficient proteins, carbohydrates, fats, water, inorganic salts, vitamins and roughage. The diet is then said to be a balanced diet.

Proteins

These are body building foods, forming the cytoplasm of cells and necessary for the building up of new tissues and for the repair of damaged tissues.

A protein molecule is very large, consisting of a large number of units known as amino acids joined together forming a long chain. There are about twenty-two different amino acids that go to make up proteins and the nature of a particular protein is determined by the number of each type of amino acid present and the order in which they are arranged in the molecule. Ten amino acids cannot be produced by the body and are essential for health. Proteins containing these ten essential amino acids are known as first class proteins, those not containing all ten essential amino acids are the second class proteins.

First class proteins—meat, fish, eggs, cheese.

Second class proteins—Most vegetable proteins, for example carrots, cabbage, beans.

Plants are able to manufacture all the amino acids they require from simple substances but animals cannot do this.

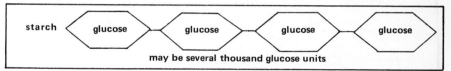

amino acids joined together forming a chain. All amino acids contain the elements carbon, hydrogen, oxygen and nitrogen. Some also contain sulphur

Carbohydrates

These are 'fuel foods', they are the compounds which are oxidised in the cells to provide energy. Carbohydrates are compounds of the elements carbon, hydrogen and oxygen.

a Monosaccharides or simple sugars.

These have the chemical formula $C_6H_{12}O_6$. Examples—glucose, fructose, fruit sugar

b Disaccharides or complex sugars.

A molecule of a disaccharide consists of two simple sugar molecules joined together, e.g. cane sugar

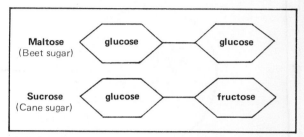

Maltose (Beet sugar)	glucose	glucose
Sucrose (Cane sugar)	glucose	fructose

c Polysaccharides.

A polysaccharide molecule consists of a great many monosaccharide molecules linked together.

starch	glucose	glucose	glucose	glucose

may be several thousand glucose units

Glycogen, Cellulose, Lignin are other examples. Bread, sugar, jam, potatoes, sweets and biscuits supply our carbohydrates.

Fats and oils

Fats and oils differ in that fats are solid at ordinary room temperatures (for example, lard), whereas oils are liquid (for example, cod liver oil). Fats and oils are like carbohydrates in that they are compounds of oxygen, hydrogen and carbon. They supply energy and are stored within the body, mainly beneath the skin and around the kidneys.

In the diet, fats are supplied by butter, margarine, lard, fatty meat.

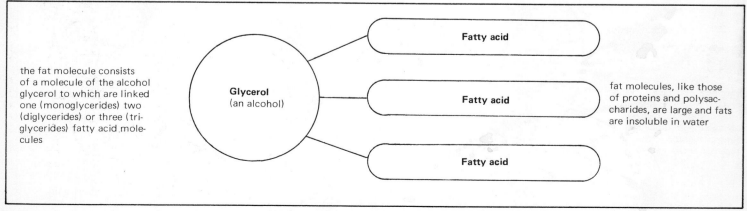

the fat molecule consists of a molecule of the alcohol glycerol to which are linked one (monoglycerides) two (diglycerides) or three (triglycerides) fatty acid molecules

Glycerol (an alcohol)

Fatty acid

Fatty acid

Fatty acid

fat molecules, like those of proteins and polysaccharides, are large and fats are insoluble in water

Energy from food

Food is the body's fuel, supplying the energy for the many activities taking place within the body. The amount of energy that a type of food can supply can be demonstrated by completely burning a known weight of the food substance and measuring how much energy (in the form of heat) is produced. The amount of heat that a food will produce when burnt can be expressed in units called kilojoules (Kj).

1000 gram of water

when 4.2Kj of heat is supplied to the water the temperature of the water will rise by 1°C

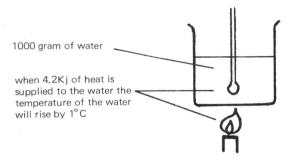

1G carbohydrate — 17Kj

1G fat — 39Kj

fat is an energy rich substance

1G protein — 17Kj

The energy value of some foods in Kj.

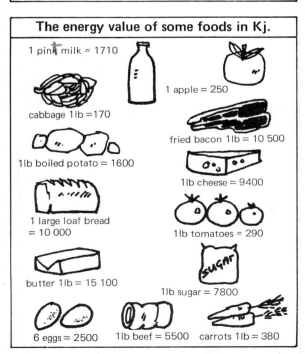

1 pink milk = 1710

1 apple = 250

cabbage 1lb = 170

fried bacon 1lb = 10 500

1lb boiled potato = 1600

1lb cheese = 9400

1 large loaf bread = 10 000

1lb tomatoes = 290

butter 1lb = 15 100

1lb sugar = 7800

6 eggs = 2500   1lb beef = 5500   carrots 1lb = 380

sleeping energy required for growth and tissue repair, digestion, excretion, secretion, production of certain substances, maintaining body temperature.

energy used when body is at rest is known as the basal metabolic rate (B.M.R.)

Adult woman

Adult man

6400Kj

7150Kj

light work 9500Kj

light work 10 500Kj

developing baby requires energy—obtained from mother's food

mother's needs during pregnancy 10 000Kj while breast feeding 12 600Kj

moderate work 13 000Kj

girl of about 8 years 6050Kj

boy of about 8 years 6700Kj

all values /24 hours

heavy manual work 15 500Kj

Vitamins and minerals

Various salts of inorganic elements are required to keep the body healthy and the table below shows some of the necessary elements, why they are required and what happens if the body lacks them. To ensure that the diet contains sufficient of these salts it should include plenty of milk, butter and cheese, whole meal bread, egg yolk, green vegetables, fruits, meat and fish.

Other elements
Sulphur, zinc, magnesium, copper, cobalt, potassium, bromine are required for special purposes.

Vitamins although essential to health are required in only very small amounts; their importance was demonstrated around 1900 by Gowland-Hopkins who found that animals fed on a diet of purified carbohydrates, protein, fat, salts and water did not grow and very rapidly died. The table below shows some of the important vitamins, foods which are rich in them, and the effect of a lack of them in the diet.

Element	Purpose for which required	Effect of deficiency
Iron	a constituent of the haemoglobin molecule	anaemia
Calcium	necessary for healthy growth of bones and teeth	rickets—bone malformation, tooth decay
Phosphorus	necessary for growth of bones and teeth and for production of A.T.P.	rickets, tooth decay
Iodine	a constituent part of the thyroxine molecule, the hormone produced by thyroid gland	simple goitre—a swelling in the neck due to enlargement of the thyroid gland
Sodium and chlorine (sodium chloride)	present in all body fluids, necessary for proper functioning of nerves and muscles	muscular cramp
Fluorine	necessary for healthy teeth. Confers resistance to decay	tooth decay

	Name of vitamin	Rich sources	Effect of deficiency
FAT SOLUBLE	A	fresh green vegetables, liver, milk, cod-liver oil, butter, carrots, yellow maize	reduced resistance to infection, dry, scaly skin, dry scaly cornea of eye i.e. xerophthalmia, night blindness
	D	cod-liver oil, egg yolk, cream. Formed in the dermis of the skin when exposed to sunlight, hence present in many animal fats.	abnormal development of bones, soft bones with swollen ends, i.e. rickets
	E	wheat embryo, green leaves, egg yolk, butter, many seed fats	it is believed to affect reproduction. Death and reabsorption of embyro in female, death of sperm in the male
WATER SOLUBLE	B$_1$	wheat embryo, yeast, peas and beans, now added to all white flour sold in Britain	Beri-beri—an inflammation of the nerves causing paralysis and wasting of arms and legs. It is fatal
	B$_2$	green vegetables, yeast, milk, meat	pellagra—digestive disturbances, loss of weight, red swellings on skin leading to death
	B$_{12}$	liver, milk, eggs, meat, fish	Pernicious anaemia—red blood cells not produced in sufficient numbers
	C	fresh uncooked vegetables, fresh fruit, especially oranges, lemons, blackcurrants and rose hips	Scurvy—bleeding beneath the skin, loosening of the teeth. Fatal
	K	spinach, cabbage	symptoms resembling those of scurvy. Delayed clotting of the blood

Water
Is an essential constituent of the diet for the following reasons.
1. Around two-thirds of the human body consists of water;
2. Water is constantly lost from the body via the kidneys, sweat glands, lungs and bowel;
3. Water takes part in many of the chemical reactions taking place within the cells and all the reactions occur in aqueous solution;
4. The products of digestion and oxygen enter the body in aqueous solution, excretory substances pass out of the body in aqueous solution.

Roughage
Some undigestible solid is necessary for the healthy functioning of the bowel.

Digestion

The large, complex molecules of proteins, fats and carbohydrates are insoluble and so cannot pass into the cells lining the gut and then through the cells into the blood capillaries surrounding the gut.

By chemical action, the large, complex molecules are digested into smaller, simpler particles which are then soluble and can be absorbed.

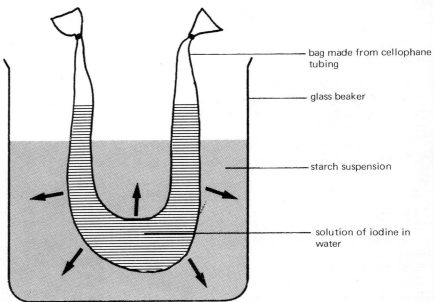

entering the mouth, solid food containing protein, fats and carbohydrates

large molecules being broken down by chemical action

products of digestion being absorbed from the intestine

alimentary canal

anus

The large complex molecules are digested in the alimentary canal by chemical reaction known as hydrolysis, i.e. by the addition of water.

For example:

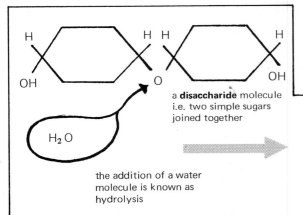

a **disaccharide** molecule i.e. two simple sugars joined together

the addition of a water molecule is known as hydrolysis

The hydrolysis reactions of digestion only takes place in the presence of special substances known as enzymes. These are all proteins produced by glands associated with the alimentary canal.

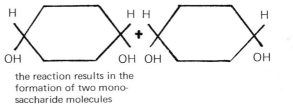

the reaction results in the formation of two mono-saccharide molecules

This experiment demonstrates the importance of digestion. Very rapidly it is found that the starch suspension in the beaker begins to show a blue-black colouration. The iodine solution in the cellophane bag however, remains unchanged in colour. Clearly the iodine particles have diffused through the minute pores in the cellophane into the surrounding starch suspension. The much larger starch molecules are too big to pass through the pores in the cellophane and therefore do not enter the bag.

bag made from cellophane tubing

glass beaker

starch suspension

solution of iodine in water

The alimentary canal

Food enters the alimentary canal by way of the mouth. In the mouth, solid food is broken into smaller pieces by means of the teeth (mastication), mixed with saliva secreted by the salivary glands and formed by means of the tongue and cheeks into a ball of food or bolus. The food bolus then passes into the oesophagus and by means of peristaltic movement passes to the stomach.

As the food passes along the alimentary canal it is acted upon by chemicals which convert the complex insoluble substances in the food into more simple substances (digestion). These products of digestion then pass from the alimentary canal into the blood (absorption), this process taking place largely from the small intestine. Substances present in the food but unable to be digested and absorbed pass on around the alimentary canal to be passed out of the body by way of the anus (defaecation).

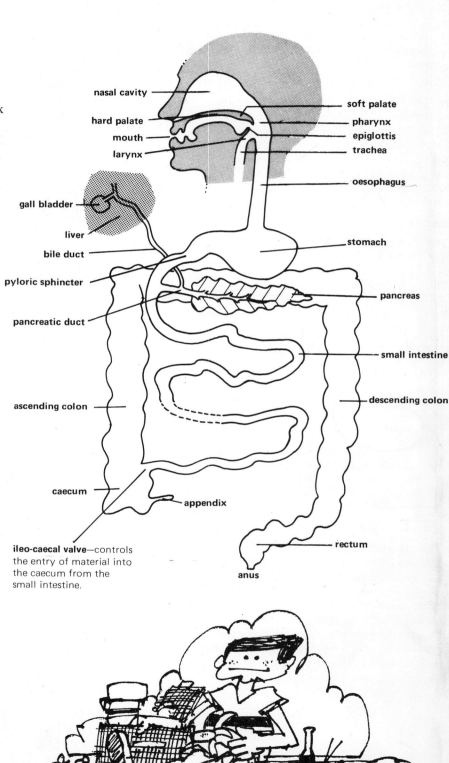

The movement of the food along the alimentary canal by muscular contraction is called peristalsis

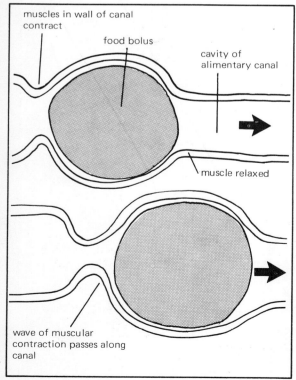

The mouth

Food taken into the mouth is broken into small pieces by means of the teeth (mastication) and mixed with saliva secreted by the salivary glands of which there are three pairs.

1 The parotid glands, just in front of and below the ear.
2 The submandibular glands, in the angle of the jaw.
3 The sub-lingual glands, below the tongue.

Saliva produced by these glands passes into the mouth by way of tubes or ducts. It consists of water together with some mucus, dissolved salts and an enzyme called ptyalin. Saliva lubricates the food to facilitate swallowing, ptyalin begins to act upon starch, catalyzing its hydrolysis to the disaccharide maltose.

Swallowing

a The tongue presses upwards and back against the roof of the mouth, pushing the food bolus to the pharynx.
b The opening between the nasal cavity and the pharynx is closed by the soft palate.
c By means of muscle action, the larynx moves upwards so that the opening into the trachea is closed by the epiglottis.
d The bolus is then pushed into and along the oesophagus by peristalsis.

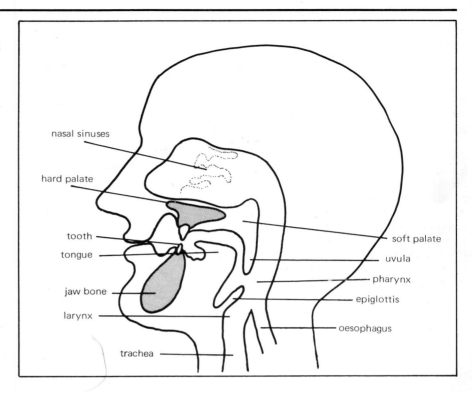

A section through a canine tooth

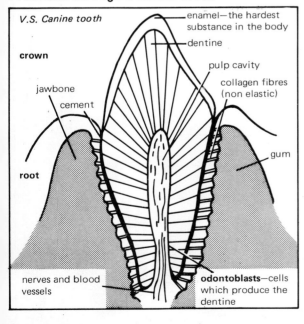

Tooth decay

Small particles of food lodged between the teeth are acted upon by bacteria which produce acid which can eat away the enamel forming holes or caries. If untreated bacteria will eventually enter the pulp cavity causing pain and the decay of the tooth.

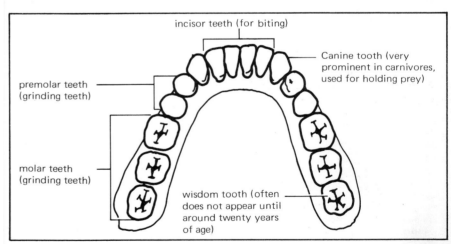

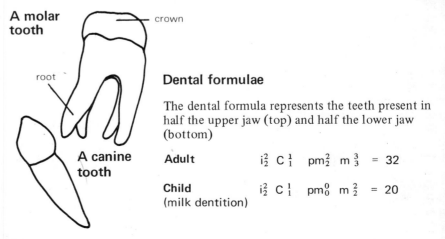

A molar tooth

A canine tooth

Dental formulae

The dental formula represents the teeth present in half the upper jaw (top) and half the lower jaw (bottom)

Adult i_2^2 C_1^1 pm_2^2 m_3^3 = 32

Child i_2^2 C_1^1 pm_0^0 m_2^2 = 20
(milk dentition)

The stomach and associated structures

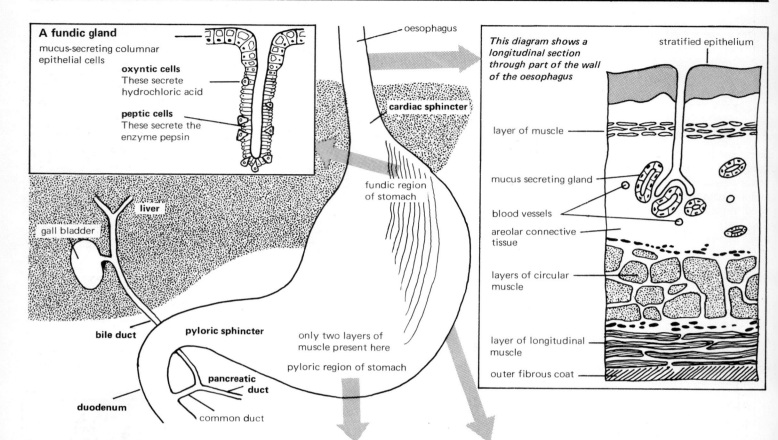

A fundic gland

mucus-secreting columnar epithelial cells

oxyntic cells
These secrete hydrochloric acid

peptic cells
These secrete the enzyme pepsin

oesophagus

cardiac sphincter

fundic region of stomach

liver

gall bladder

bile duct

pyloric sphincter

only two layers of muscle present here

pyloric region of stomach

pancreatic duct

duodenum

common duct

This diagram shows a longitudinal section through part of the wall of the oesophagus

stratified epithelium

layer of muscle

mucus secreting gland

blood vessels

areolar connective tissue

layers of circular muscle

layer of longitudinal muscle

outer fibrous coat

Food having passed down the oesophagus by peristalsis, enters the stomach when the muscles of the cardiac sphincter relax. In the stomach the food is churned up by means of muscular contraction and mixed with gastric juice.

Gastric Juice

secreted by glands in stomach wall contains:-
1 Water
2 Hydrochloric acid–neutralises alkaline saliva, kills bacteria.
3 The enzyme pepsin–catalyses hydrolysis of proteins to peptones, i.e. shorter chains of amino acids
4 Mucus–prevents damage of stomach lining by gastric juice.

Food remains within the stomach for between one and four and a half hours. It becomes converted into a milky-paste-like substance called chyme.

The stomach produces a compound known as the intrinsic factor. This is necessary for the absorption of vitamin B12. Vitamin B12 is essential for the production of red blood cells in the bone marrow.

Alcohol and some drugs are absorbed directly into the blood from the stomach.

Although rennin is present in the gastric secretion of many mammals, it is now thought not to be present in man. The clotting of milk is brought about by the action of the hydrochloric acid and pepsin.

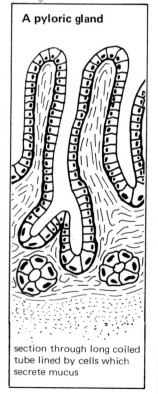

A pyloric gland

section through long coiled tube lined by cells which secrete mucus

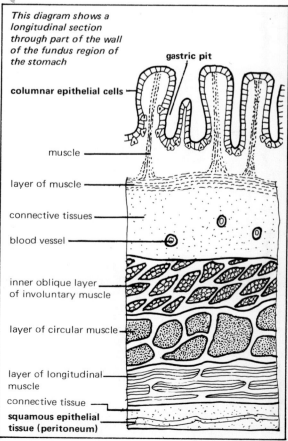

This diagram shows a longitudinal section through part of the wall of the fundus region of the stomach

gastric pit

columnar epithelial cells

muscle

layer of muscle

connective tissues

blood vessel

inner oblique layer of involuntary muscle

layer of circular muscle

layer of longitudinal muscle

connective tissue

squamous epithelial tissue (peritoneum)

The intestines

Bile

Bile is green due to the presence of two coloured substances or pigments bilirubin and biliverdin. These are breakdown products of the red pigment haemoglobin. Bile is produced in the liver. It is a green, bitter tasting liquid containing dissolved salts which make it alkaline.

gall bladder
bile stored here

bile duct

Food passes from pyloric region of stomach through plyloric sphincter to enter the duodenum

pancreatic duct

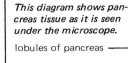

pancreas

duodenum

This diagram shows pancreas tissue as it is seen under the microscope.

lobules of pancreas

blood vessel

branch of the pancreatic duct

Islets of Langerhans
these secrete the hormone insulin. Groups of cells which secrete pancreatic juice

The duodenum

Food entering the duodenum from the stomach is mixed with the secretions of two glands.

1. Pancreatic juice secreted by the pancreas contains:

a Water
b Dissolved alkaline salts—neutralise acid from stomach, provide an alkaline medium for the enzymes of pancreatic juice.
c Lipase—catalyses the hydrolysis of fats to glycerol and fatty acids.
d Amylase—catalyses the hydrolysis of starch to maltose.
e Trypsinogen—activated by enterokinase of intestinal juice to become trypsin which catalyses hydrolysis of peptones to form very short amino acid chains called polypeptides.

2. Bile, secreted by liver. Its function is to cause fat droplets to be broken up into many smaller droplets i.e. emulsification.

Greatly increase surface on which lipase can act.

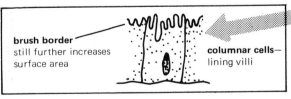

brush border
still further increases surface area

columnar cells—
lining villi

small intestine
a 22ft very coiled tube

Transverse section

Very folded inner lining to increase surface area

This diagram shows a single villus

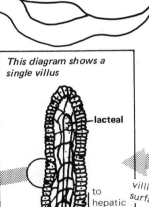

lacteal

to hepatic portal vein

by muscle action villi constantly elongate and shorten

capillaries
sugar and amino acids enter the blood directly

columnar epithelium

villi greatly increase surface area

muscle layer

intestinal glands which secrete intestinal juice

connective tissue and blood vessels

layer of circular muscle

layer of longitudinal muscle

peritoneum—squamous epithelium

The small intestine

In the small intestine, the partially digested food is acted upon by intestinal juice secreted by the intestinal glands.

Contents:

a water
b dissolved salts
c enterokinase—activates trypsin
d erepsin—polypeptides to amino acids
e lipase—fats to glycerol and fatty acids
f invertase—sucrose to glucose and fructose
g lactase—lactose to glucose and galactose
h maltase—maltose to glucose

The large intestine

Functions—as the undigested material passes by peritalsis along the large intestine, water is absorbed from it so that the faeces are relatively dry.

Some glucose is also absorbed and also some salts. There are large numbers of bacteria present some of which can produce vitamins B and K.

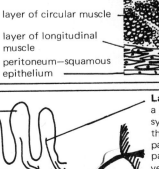

Villi

glucose, fructose, galactose, and amino acids are taken in the blood through the hepatic portal vein to the liver

Lacteal
a branch of the lymphatic system. Fats absorbed by the cells lining the villus pass into the lacteal then pass through the lymphatic vessels to the region of the neck where the fats enter the blood

The Liver

The liver is the largest gland in the body, the weight of the liver in the average man is 1.4 to 1.6 kg, and in the average woman from 1.2 to 1.4 kg,

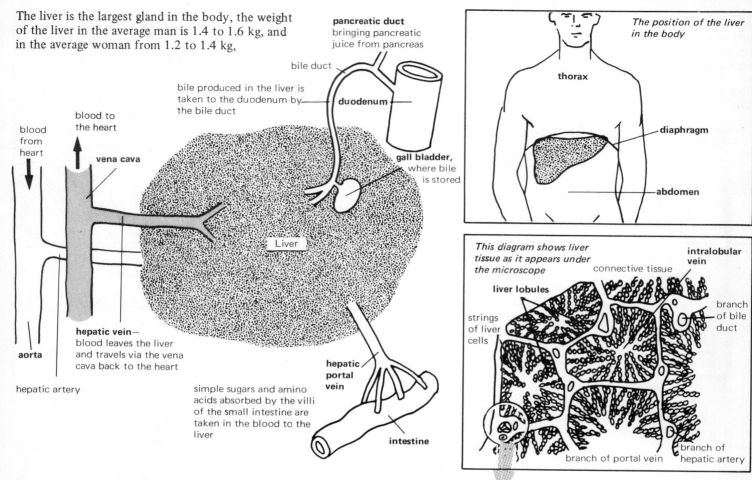

pancreatic duct bringing pancreatic juice from pancreas

bile duct

bile produced in the liver is taken to the duodenum by the bile duct

duodenum

gall bladder, where bile is stored

The position of the liver in the body

thorax

diaphragm

abdomen

blood to the heart

blood from heart

vena cava

Liver

hepatic vein— blood leaves the liver and travels via the vena cava back to the heart

aorta

hepatic artery

simple sugars and amino acids absorbed by the villi of the small intestine are taken in the blood to the liver

hepatic portal vein

intestine

This diagram shows liver tissue as it appears under the microscope

intralobular vein

connective tissue

liver lobules

strings of liver cells

branch of bile duct

branch of portal vein

branch of hepatic artery

Summary of the functions of the liver.

1 Production of bile.
2 Storage of carbohydrate in the form of the polysaccharide glycogen. The release of carbohydrate as glucose when necessary.
3 The breaking down of excess amino acid, a process known as deamination.

Amino group removed ie. deamination.

$$NH_2 \rightarrow \text{an amino acid} \rightarrow \text{acid part} + NH_3 \text{ ammonia}$$

the amino group

used in respiration.

$$2 NH_3 + CO_2 \longrightarrow CO(NH_2)_2 + H_2O$$

very poisonous

urea - excreted via the kidneys

4 The production of heat.
5 The breaking down of some hormones, drugs, alcohol and toxic substances.
6 Manufacture of the haemotinic principle, necessary for the production of the red blood cells in the bone marrow.
7 The storage of blood.
8 The breakdown of haemoglobin.
9 Storage of iron, copper and vitamins A,D and B12.

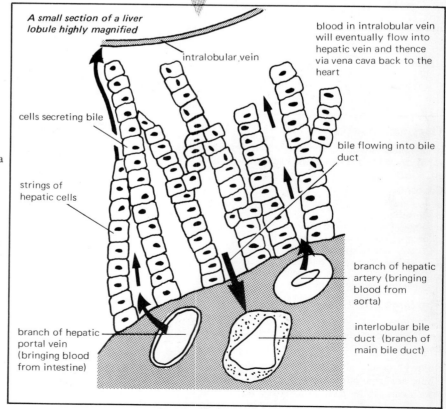

A small section of a liver lobule highly magnified

blood in intralobular vein will eventually flow into hepatic vein and thence via vena cava back to the heart

intralobular vein

cells secreting bile

bile flowing into bile duct

strings of hepatic cells

branch of hepatic artery (bringing blood from aorta)

branch of hepatic portal vein (bringing blood from intestine)

interlobular bile duct (branch of main bile duct)

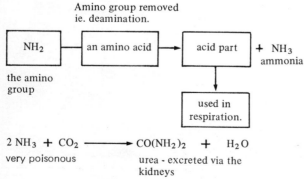

Plants make our food

All work activities taking place within our cells require energy. All energy comes originally from the sun, travelling across space in the form of light energy.

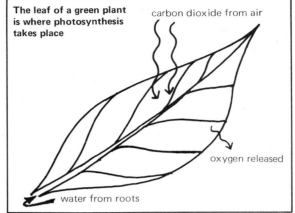

The leaf of a green plant is where photosynthesis takes place

carbon dioxide from air

oxygen released

water from roots

photosynthesis is the name of the vitally important process by which the energy of sunlight, in the presence of the green substance chlorophyll water and carbon dioxide is used to make carbohydrates

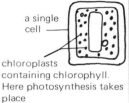

a single cell

chloroplasts containing chlorophyll. Here photosynthesis takes place

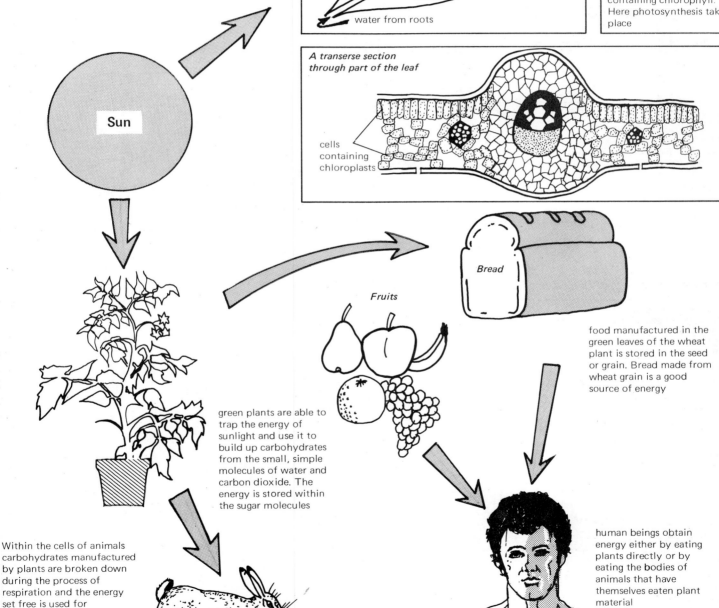

A transerse section through part of the leaf

cells containing chloroplasts

Sun

Bread

Fruits

green plants are able to trap the energy of sunlight and use it to build up carbohydrates from the small, simple molecules of water and carbon dioxide. The energy is stored within the sugar molecules

food manufactured in the green leaves of the wheat plant is stored in the seed or grain. Bread made from wheat grain is a good source of energy

Within the cells of animals carbohydrates manufactured by plants are broken down during the process of respiration and the energy set free is used for carrying out the work of the cell

human beings obtain energy either by eating plants directly or by eating the bodies of animals that have themselves eaten plant material

Respiration

The lungs

This chapter is concerned with how the body makes substances containing lots of energy. In order to do this efficiently, oxygen is needed.

The process whereby oxygen is absorbed from the atmosphere and carried to the tissues is called external respiration. The chemical reactions occuring within the cells is tissue or internal respiration.

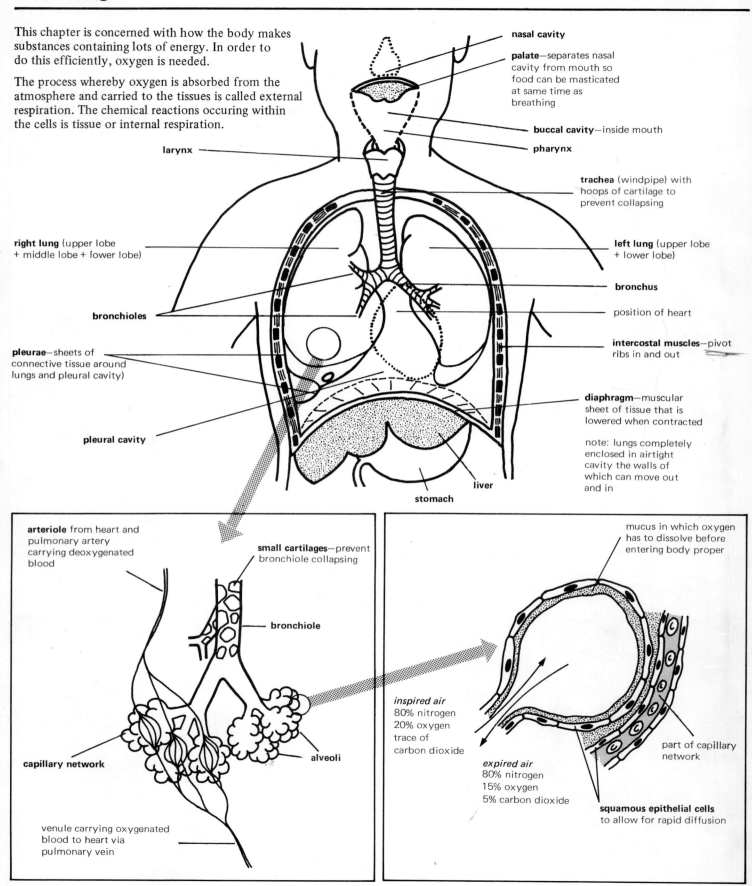

nasal cavity

palate—separates nasal cavity from mouth so food can be masticated at same time as breathing

buccal cavity—inside mouth

pharynx

larynx

trachea (windpipe) with hoops of cartilage to prevent collapsing

right lung (upper lobe + middle lobe + lower lobe)

left lung (upper lobe + lower lobe)

bronchus

position of heart

bronchioles

intercostal muscles—pivot ribs in and out

pleurae—sheets of connective tissue around lungs and pleural cavity)

diaphragm—muscular sheet of tissue that is lowered when contracted

note: lungs completely enclosed in airtight cavity the walls of which can move out and in

pleural cavity

liver

stomach

arteriole from heart and pulmonary artery carrying deoxygenated blood

small cartilages—prevent bronchiole collapsing

bronchiole

capillary network

alveoli

venule carrying oxygenated blood to heart via pulmonary vein

mucus in which oxygen has to dissolve before entering body proper

inspired air
80% nitrogen
20% oxygen
trace of carbon dioxide

expired air
80% nitrogen
15% oxygen
5% carbon dioxide

part of capillary network

squamous epithelial cells to allow for rapid diffusion

Chest movement (breathing)

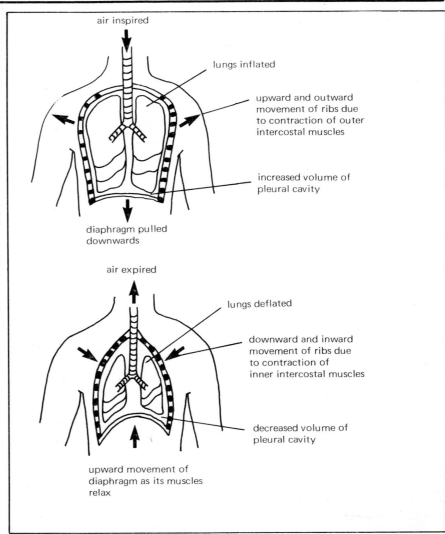

hypodermic Syringe

pressure outside greater
than at "A"

fluid sucked in

"A"

downward movement of
piston increases volume
of "A"

the reverse happens to
expel the fluid

air inspired

lungs inflated

upward and outward
movement of ribs due
to contraction of outer
intercostal muscles

increased volume of
pleural cavity

diaphragm pulled
downwards

air expired

lungs deflated

downward and inward
movement of ribs due
to contraction of
inner intercostal muscles

decreased volume of
pleural cavity

upward movement of
diaphragm as its muscles
relax

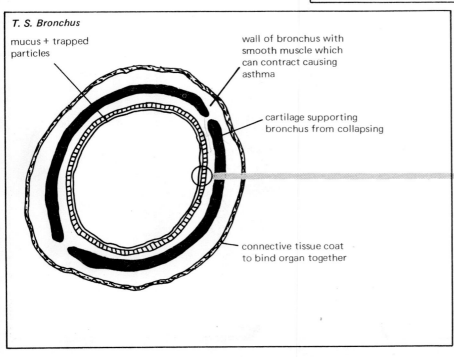

T. S. Bronchus

mucus + trapped
particles

wall of bronchus with
smooth muscle which
can contract causing
asthma

cartilage supporting
bronchus from collapsing

connective tissue coat
to bind organ together

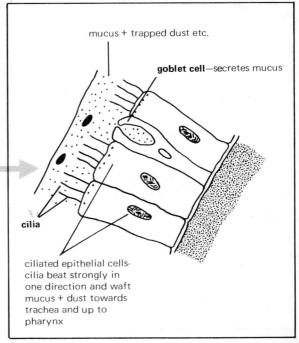

mucus + trapped dust etc.

goblet cell—secretes mucus

cilia

ciliated epithelial cells-
cilia beat strongly in
one direction and waft
mucus + dust towards
trachea and up to
pharynx

Gas exchange

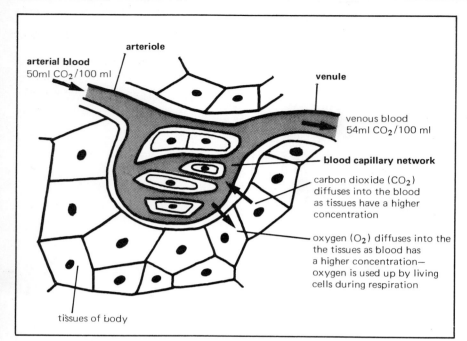

arteriole

arterial blood
50ml CO_2/100 ml

venule

venous blood
54ml CO_2/100 ml

blood capillary network

carbon dioxide (CO_2)
diffuses into the blood
as tissues have a higher
concentration

oxygen (O_2) diffuses into the
the tissues as blood has
a higher concentration—
oxygen is used up by living
cells during respiration

tissues of body

All gases passively diffuse from the region of high
concentration to the region of low concentration.
No energy (ATP) is used up:

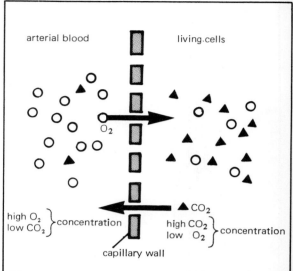

arterial blood

living.cells

O_2

high O_2
low CO_2 } concentration

CO_2

high CO_2
low O_2 } concentration

capillary wall

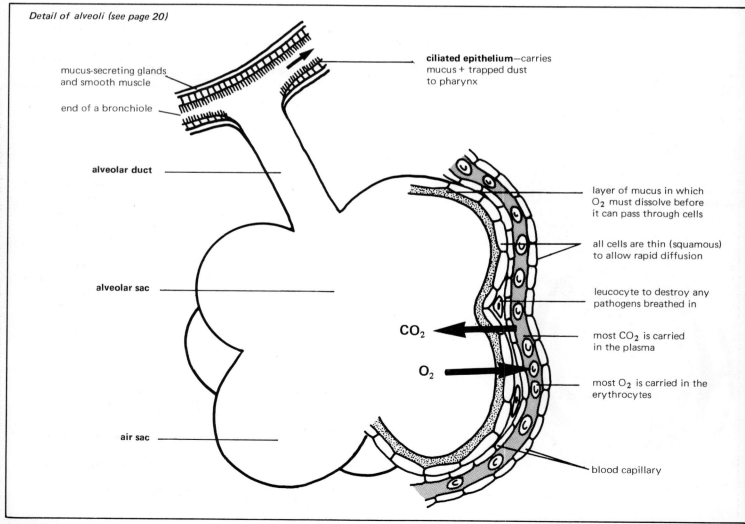

Detail of alveoli (see page 20)

mucus-secreting glands
and smooth muscle

end of a bronchiole

ciliated epithelium—carries
mucus + trapped dust
to pharynx

alveolar duct

layer of mucus in which
O_2 must dissolve before
it can pass through cells

all cells are thin (squamous)
to allow rapid diffusion

alveolar sac

leucocyte to destroy any
pathogens breathed in

CO_2

most CO_2 is carried
in the plasma

O_2

most O_2 is carried in the
erythrocytes

air sac

blood capillary

Oxygen

Normal oxygen dissociation curve

% saturation of haemoglobin with oxygen

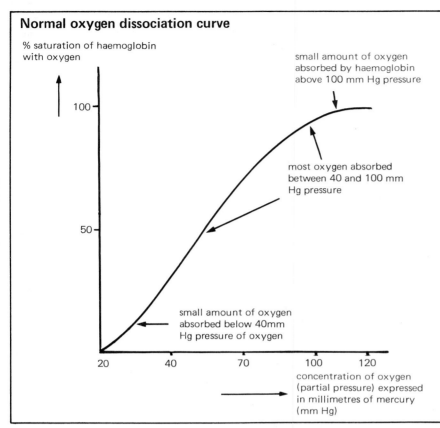

small amount of oxygen absorbed by haemoglobin above 100 mm Hg pressure

most oxygen absorbed between 40 and 100 mm Hg pressure

small amount of oxygen absorbed below 40mm Hg pressure of oxygen

concentration of oxygen (partial pressure) expressed in millimetres of mercury (mm Hg)

Note:
The air in the alveoli contains approximately 100mm pressure of oxygen so the haemoglobin becomes nearly saturated with oxygen. The body cells have a concentration of about 40 mm of oxygen so most oxygen leaves the blood and passes into these cells.

N.B. When cells respire more vigorously, e.g. when exercising, the blood temperature rises and more CO_2 is given out. This means that more O_2 is given up by blood to tissues.

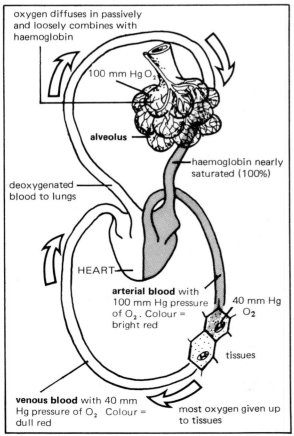

oxygen diffuses in passively and loosely combines with haemoglobin

100 mm Hg O_2

alveolus

haemoglobin nearly saturated (100%)

deoxygenated blood to lungs

HEART

arterial blood with 100 mm Hg pressure of O_2. Colour = bright red

40 mm Hg O_2

tissues

most oxygen given up to tissues

venous blood with 40 mm Hg pressure of O_2 Colour = dull red

Abnormal oxygen dissociation curve

percent saturation of haemoglobin with oxygen

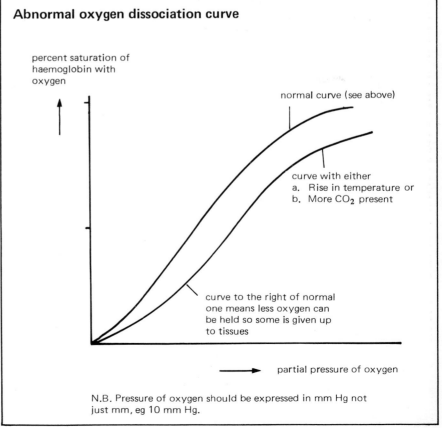

normal curve (see above)

curve with either
a. Rise in temperature or
b. More CO_2 present

curve to the right of normal one means less oxygen can be held so some is given up to tissues

partial pressure of oxygen

N.B. Pressure of oxygen should be expressed in mm Hg not just mm, eg 10 mm Hg.

Breathing

Breathing Capacity

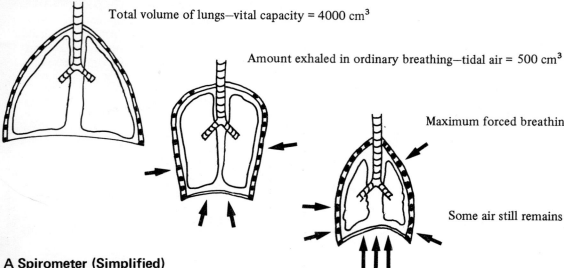

Total volume of lungs—vital capacity = 4000 cm³

Amount exhaled in ordinary breathing—tidal air = 500 cm³

Maximum forced breathing—complemental air = 3000 cm³

Some air still remains in lungs—residual air = 1000 cm³

A Spirometer (Simplified)

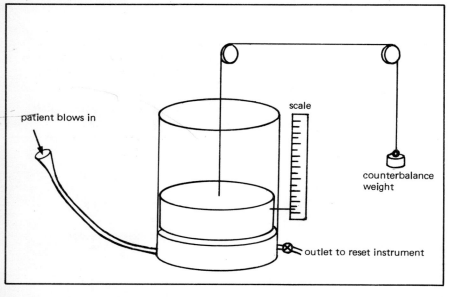

patient blows in

scale

counterbalance weight

outlet to reset instrument

A spirometer is used to measure the vital capacity etc. of patients in order to help diagnose certain respiratory and cardiac diseases. (See photograph on page 138).

Normal vital capacities vary with age, sex and occupation:

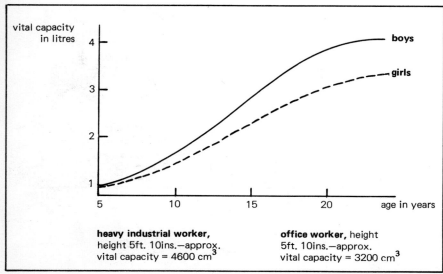

vital capacity in litres

boys

girls

age in years

heavy industrial worker, height 5ft. 10ins.—approx. vital capacity = 4600 cm³

office worker, height 5ft. 10ins.—approx. vital capacity = 3200 cm³

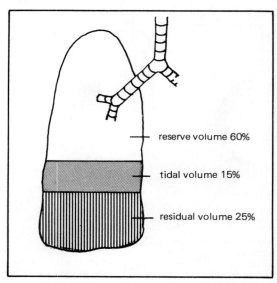

reserve volume 60%

tidal volume 15%

residual volume 25%

Regulation of breathing

A. Subconscious Control (Normal)

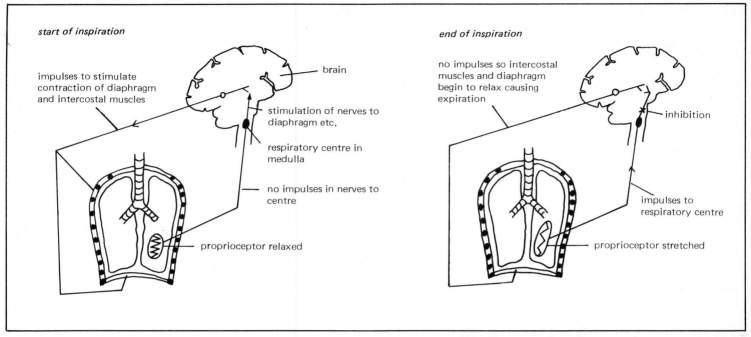

start of inspiration

impulses to stimulate contraction of diaphragm and intercostal muscles

brain

stimulation of nerves to diaphragm etc.

respiratory centre in medulla

no impulses in nerves to centre

proprioceptor relaxed

end of inspiration

no impulses so intercostal muscles and diaphragm begin to relax causing expiration

inhibition

impulses to respiratory centre

proprioceptor stretched

B. Conscious Control
For forced breathing at willed rate and depth

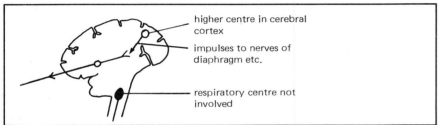

higher centre in cerebral cortex

impulses to nerves of diaphragm etc.

respiratory centre not involved

N.B. This is a self-regulating mechanism as are most actions within the body. Homeostasis is the term given to such actions.

C. Rapid Normal Breathing

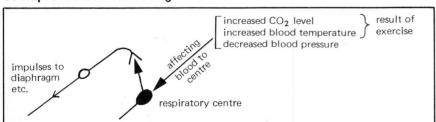

impulses to diaphragm etc.

affecting blood to centre

increased CO_2 level
increased blood temperature
decreased blood pressure
} result of exercise

respiratory centre

D. Coughing
Usually a simple reflex action not under control of will

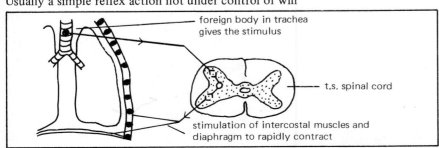

foreign body in trachea gives the stimulus

t.s. spinal cord

stimulation of intercostal muscles and diaphragm to rapidly contract

COUGH

Common diseases of the respiratory system

Usual symptoms of these diseases, if severe, are:
1. mucous congestion
2. increased respiratory rate
3. coughing due to irritation
4. dyspnoea—breathlessness

5. coughing blood—in severest cases
6. heart rate affected
7. pain in chest
8. cyanosis—blueing of skin

Inflammation of linings
due to action of bacteria:

tonsillitis

pharyngitis

laryngitis

bronchitis

broncho-pneumonia

pneumonia

Other diseases

acute coryza—common cold—virus infection—secondary infections of bacteria often occur

pleurisy—infection of pleurae

lung cancer—bronchus wall stimulated to grow abnormally causing carcinoma

bronchial asthma—spasms of bronchial wall due to an allergy

pulmonary tuberculosis—bacteria invade lungs and stimulate cysts to develop—tissues die leaving spaces

Normal rates after resting

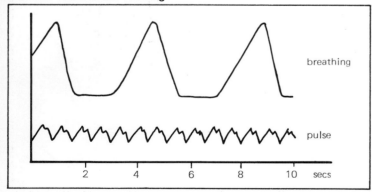

breathing

pulse

Rates after some exercise

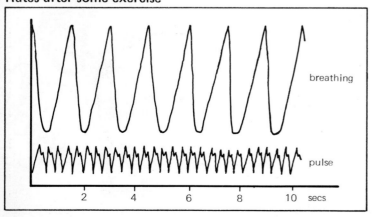

breathing

pulse

Person suffering with heart or respiratory disease

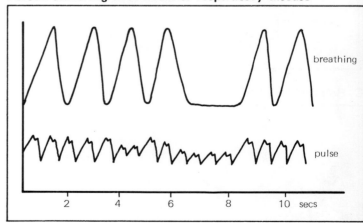

breathing

pulse

The respiratory rate and the pulse rate usually influence each other—see symptom 6. of respiratory diseases and notes on the respirometer.

N.B. see also diagrams of artificial respiration in section on first aid.

Internal or tissue respiration

How the living cells of the body use the oxygen which is obtained, via the lungs and taken by the blood in the arteries to the tissues of the body.

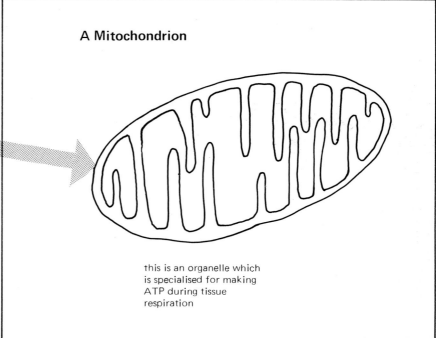

glucose obtained by nutrition and absorbed by all living cells

oxygen obtained by external respiration (breathing)

excreted carbon dioxide + water

ENERGY stored in the form of ATP and subsequently used for all life processes

Note: Diagrams of organelles, cells and tissues should always be compared with photographs of the actual specimens.

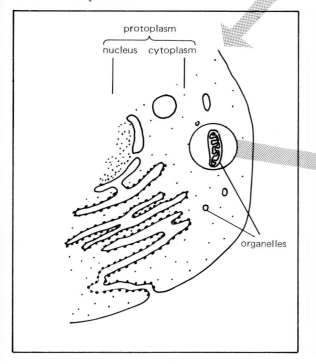

protoplasm

nucleus cytoplasm

organelles

A Mitochondrion

this is an organelle which is specialised for making ATP during tissue respiration

The Two Stages of Tissue Respiration

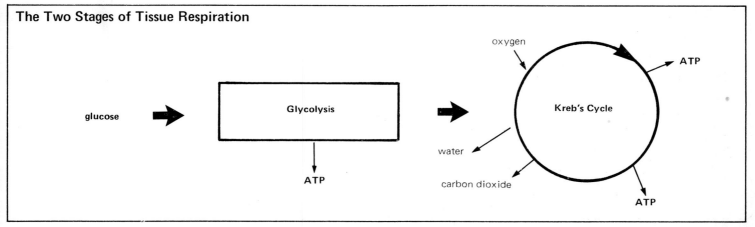

glucose

Glycolysis

ATP

oxygen

Kreb's Cycle

ATP

water

carbon dioxide

ATP

A.T.P. and anaerobic respiration

A.T.P. = Adenosine Triphosphate

This is how the body stores energy for immediate use.

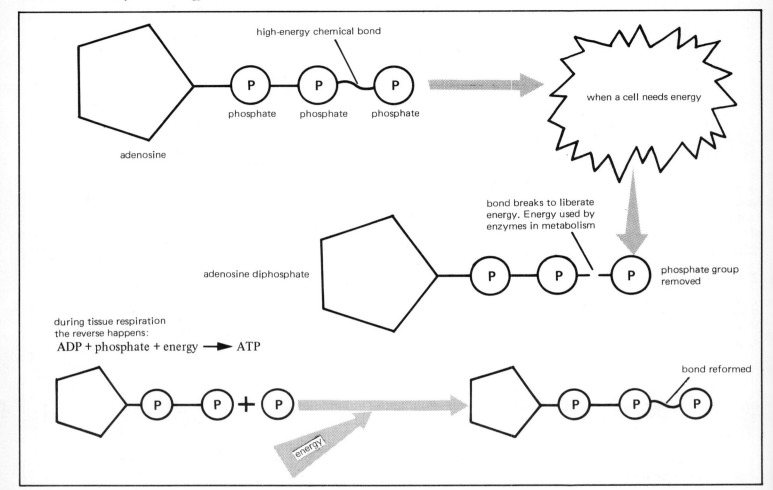

The energy from tissue respiration is therefore
temporarily stored as chemical bond energy
and ATP is formed.

1. Anaerobic Respiration

1. takes place in cytoplasm
2. no oxygen used
3. very little ATP formed
4. wasteful process
5. when oxygen in short supply, e.g. during violent
   exercise, some cells can perform glycolysis without
   the Kreb's cycle and produce some ATP. This also
   applies to some yeasts and bacteria. The process is
   called anaerobic respiration as no oxygen is needed.

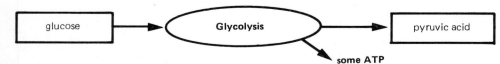

Note: The reader is advised to consult the syllabus
he is studying as not all call for as much detail as
shown above.

A.T.P. and anaerobic respiration

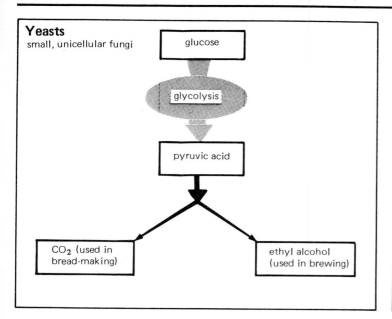

Yeasts
small, unicellular fungi

glucose → glycolysis → pyruvic acid → CO₂ (used in bread-making) / ethyl alcohol (used in brewing)

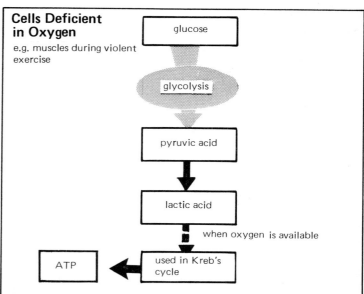

Cells Deficient in Oxygen
e.g. muscles during violent exercise

glucose → glycolysis → pyruvic acid → lactic acid → when oxygen is available → used in Kreb's cycle → ATP

2. Aerobic Respiration

1. takes place in mitochondria
2. oxygen absorbed through lungs used up
3. water and carbon dioxide are waste products
4. very efficient as lot of ATP made

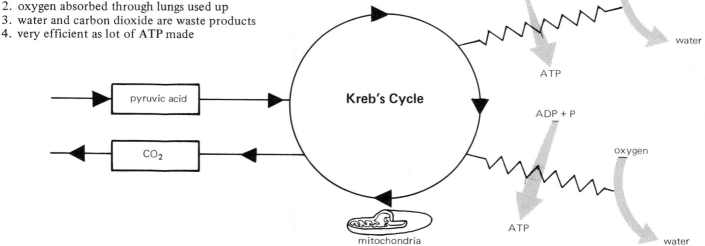

The whole process of tissue respiration can be summarised as follows:

$$C_6H_{12}O_6 + 6O_2 \rightarrow 6CO_2 + 6H_2O + ATP$$

glucose   oxygen   carbon dioxide   water   energy

Glycolysis, the Kreb's cycle and making ATP are performed in many stages.
Each stage is controlled by an enzyme and results in the loss of some energy. Where the energy loss is great, ATP is formed.

Photosynthesis is the reverse of this process—substances containing little energy (CO_2 and H_2O) are converted to substances with lots of energy (e.g. glucose).

All metabolic pathways, like tissue respiration, are controlled by enzymes and ATP is involved in nearly all of them.

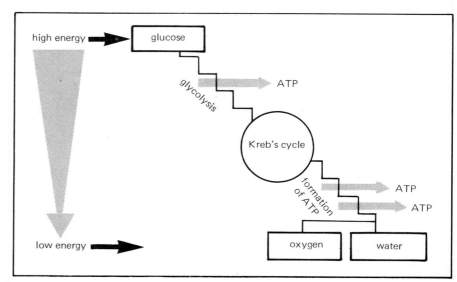

Blood

Structure of blood

Platelets (thrombocytes)—
bits of cells—see notes on clotting

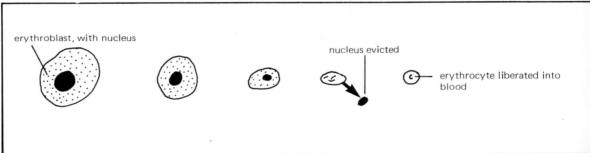

t.s. erythrocyte

Plasma
90% water
7-8% protein
1% salts
2% food substances

plasma minus
fibrinogen = serum

Erythrocyte (red corpuscle)

1. No nucleus so cytoplasm can contain more haemoglobin.
2. Fixed life—about 3 months. Broken down by spleen and liver and partly used to make bile.
3. Made in red bone marrow of larger bones of body.
4. Stored in spleen till needed.
5. Its membrane is elastic so can squeeze through narrow capillaries.
6. Biconcave giving it a large surface area for gas exchange.
7. Number per cubic millilitre of blood:
   men   — 5 400 000
   women   — 4 800 000   varies as to health

Leucocyte (white corpuscle)

1. Nucleus present so no fixed life.
2. Can change shape and move against blood flow.
3. Able to squeeze through capillary walls and enter tissues.
4. Formed by mitosis of parent white corpuscles.
5. Several kinds.

Stages in formation of erythrocytes in red bone marrow

erythroblast, with nucleus

nucleus evicted

erythrocyte liberated into blood

Types of leucocytes

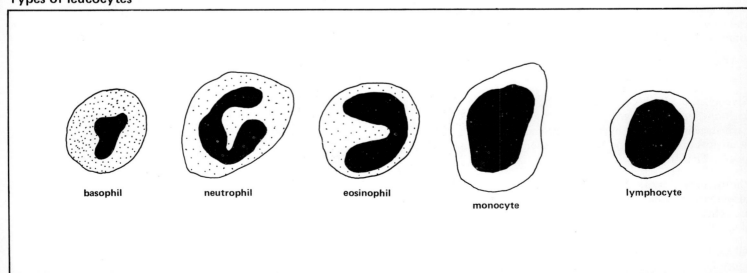

basophil   neutrophil   eosinophil   monocyte   lymphocyte

Note: not necessary to learn types

Functions of the blood

Functions of the Blood

Blood is a transport system to circulate essential substances around the body and carry excretory products from living cells to excretory organs. It has other functions: preventing pathogens (disease-causing organisms) entering and multiplying and also temperature control.

BLOOD DONORS LTD.

1) dissipating heat, chiefly from muscles and the gut, to all the body

2) transporting oxygen from the lungs to all body cells

5) transporting carbon dioxide and water waste from body cells to the lungs

6) transporting urea waste from the liver to the kidneys

7) transporting absorbed food from the small intestine to the liver and thence to all body cells

8) stimulating sweat glands to function and cool the blood

3) circulating hormones from endocrine glands throughout the body

4) clotting to seal wounds. Destroying invading organisms

How blood functions

1. Dissipating heat

Warm and cool blood are mixed in the heart so blood
temperature of 37° C (98.4° F) is the same throughout
body. Water (and blood) is an ideal distributor as it
has high specific heat:

1 It needs lots of heat to warm it up, so it can carry
   lots of heat away.
2 It gives up heat slowly so prevents organs which
   must be cool e.g. testes, being damaged by too
   much heat.

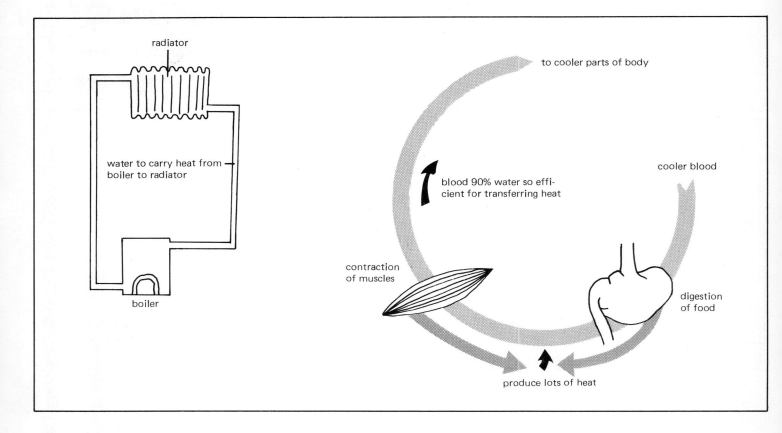

2. Transport of Oxygen

(see notes on gaseous exchange
during respiration)

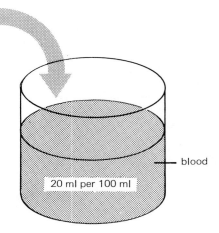

Up to 60 times more oxygen can be carried by blood
than water because haemoglobin is present in
erythrocytes.

How blood functions

Diagram of Haemoglobin

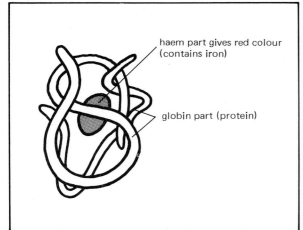

haem part gives red colour (contains iron)

globin part (protein)

Oxyhaemoglobin (bright red, as in arteries)

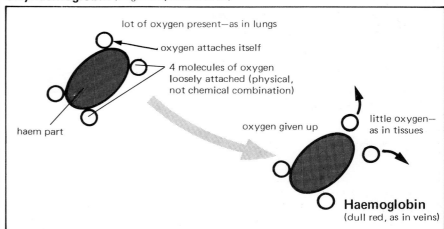

lot of oxygen present—as in lungs

oxygen attaches itself

4 molecules of oxygen loosely attached (physical, not chemical combination)

haem part

oxygen given up

little oxygen— as in tissues

Haemoglobin
(dull red, as in veins)

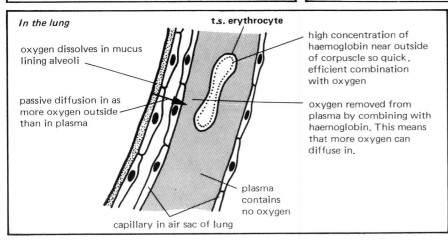

In the lung

t.s. erythrocyte

oxygen dissolves in mucus lining alveoli

passive diffusion in as more oxygen outside than in plasma

high concentration of haemoglobin near outside of corpuscle so quick, efficient combination with oxygen

oxygen removed from plasma by combining with haemoglobin. This means that more oxygen can diffuse in.

plasma contains no oxygen

capillary in air sac of lung

Erythrocytes are also concerned with the transport of carbon dioxide. See notes on gaseous exchange.

3. Transporting Hormones

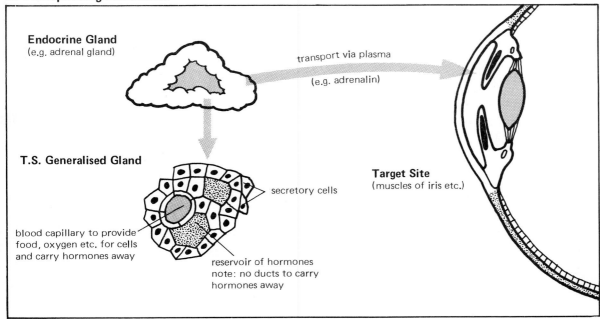

Endocrine Gland
(e.g. adrenal gland)

transport via plasma
(e.g. adrenalin)

T.S. Generalised Gland

secretory cells

blood capillary to provide food, oxygen etc. for cells and carry hormones away

reservoir of hormones note: no ducts to carry hormones away

Target Site
(muscles of iris etc.)

The two kinds of hormone—protein derived and fat derived—are both transported in the blood plasma.

How blood functions 2

4 Clotting

1) Seals wounds to prevent blood escaping and pathogens entering.
2) Protects damaged tissues underneath to allow unhindered new growth and replacement.
   a) Fibrin not normally present in plasma but a precursor, fibrinogen, is.
   b) An enzyme, thrombin, converts fibrinogen to fibrin which then traps corpuscles forming a clot.
   c) Thrombin is not usually present in the plasma but an inactive form, prothrombin, is.
   d) Two substances are needed to activate prothrombin—calcium ions (present in the plasma) and an enzyme, thromboplastin.
   e) Thromboplastin is only formed when a tissue or blood vessel is damaged. This then sets up a chain reaction and a clot forms where the tissue is damaged.

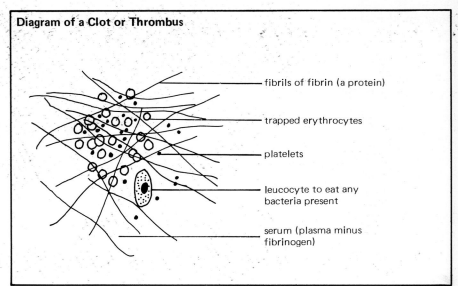

Diagram of a Clot or Thrombus

- fibrils of fibrin (a protein)
- trapped erythrocytes
- platelets
- leucocyte to eat any bacteria present
- serum (plasma minus fibrinogen)

Summary of Clotting Process

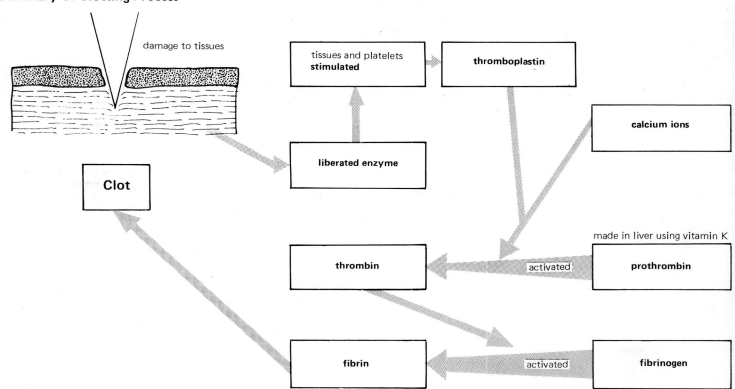

damage to tissues

tissues and platelets **stimulated**

thromboplastin

calcium ions

liberated enzyme

Clot

made in liver using vitamin K

thrombin ← activated ← **prothrombin**

fibrin ← activated ← **fibrinogen**

Normally in Plasma

An anticoagulant prevents a clot forming. It works by preventing one of the above substances acting e.g. citric acid and sodium citrate added to donated blood as they combine with calcium making it unavailable for activating prothrombin.

A clot inside an artery or vein—an embolism—stops the flow of blood. this can be fatal especially in an artery to the brain or heart muscles as the oxygen supply is cut off causing a stroke or a coronary thrombosis.

How blood functions 3

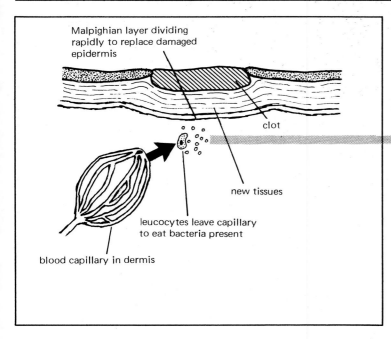

Malpighian layer dividing rapidly to replace damaged epidermis

clot

new tissues

leucocytes leave capillary to eat bacteria present

blood capillary in dermis

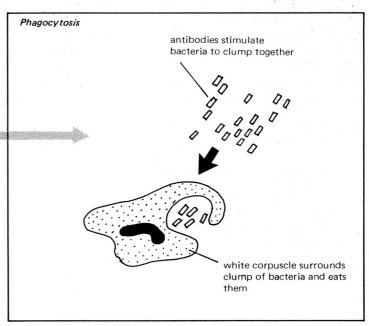

Phagocytosis

antibodies stimulate bacteria to clump together

white corpuscle surrounds clump of bacteria and eats them

5 Transport of Carbon Dioxide and Water

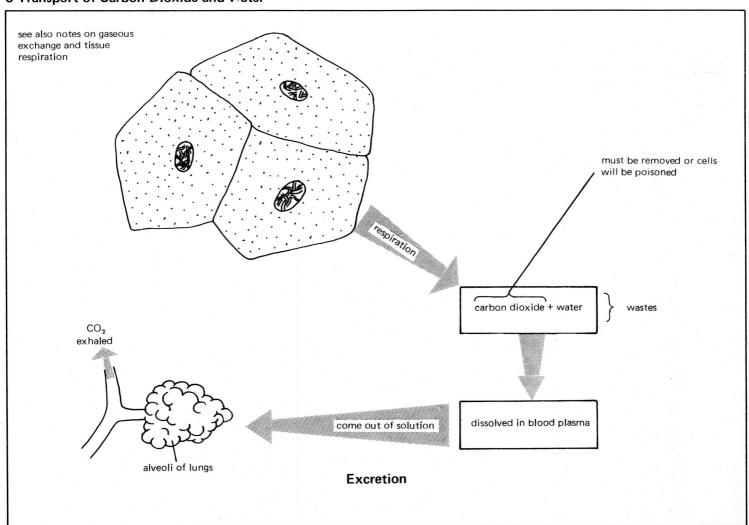

see also notes on gaseous exchange and tissue respiration

respiration

must be removed or cells will be poisoned

carbon dioxide + water } wastes

CO_2 exhaled

come out of solution

dissolved in blood plasma

alveoli of lungs

Excretion

How blood functions 4

6. Urea Transport

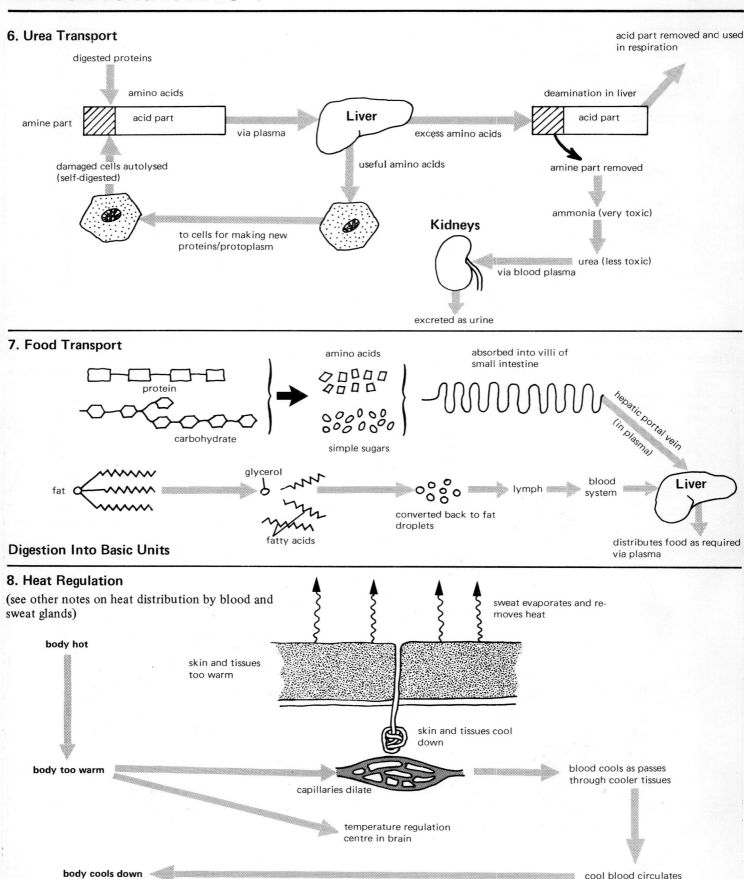

digested proteins

amino acids

amine part | acid part

via plasma

Liver

excess amino acids

deamination in liver

acid part

acid part removed and used in respiration

amine part removed

ammonia (very toxic)

damaged cells autolysed (self-digested)

useful amino acids

Kidneys

urea (less toxic)

via blood plasma

to cells for making new proteins/protoplasm

excreted as urine

7. Food Transport

protein

carbohydrate

amino acids

simple sugars

absorbed into villi of small intestine

hepatic portal vein (in plasma)

fat

glycerol

fatty acids

converted back to fat droplets

lymph

blood system

Liver

distributes food as required via plasma

Digestion Into Basic Units

8. Heat Regulation

(see other notes on heat distribution by blood and sweat glands)

body hot

skin and tissues too warm

sweat evaporates and removes heat

skin and tissues cool down

body too warm

capillaries dilate

blood cools as passes through cooler tissues

temperature regulation centre in brain

body cools down

cool blood circulates

Blood circulation

General Plan

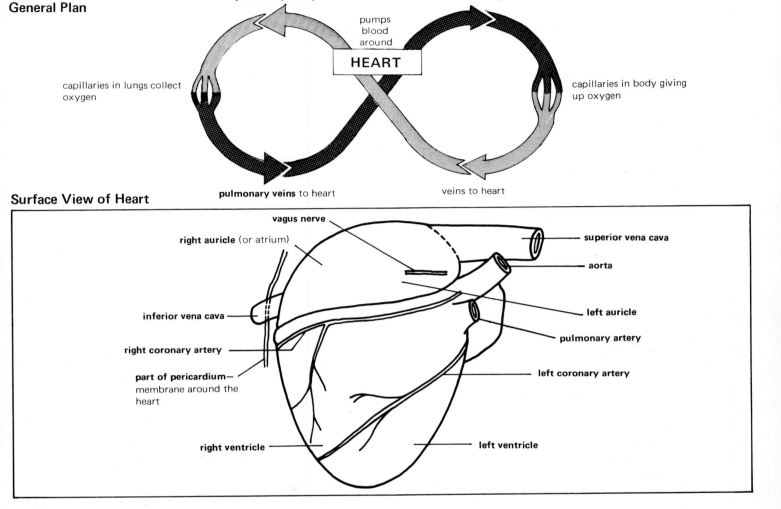

pumps blood around
HEART

pulmonary artery   **aorta** to body

capillaries in lungs collect oxygen

capillaries in body giving up oxygen

pulmonary veins to heart   veins to heart

Surface View of Heart

vagus nerve

right auricle (or atrium)

superior vena cava

aorta

inferior vena cava

left auricle

pulmonary artery

right coronary artery

part of pericardium— membrane around the heart

left coronary artery

right ventricle   **left ventricle**

Diagrammatic Section to Show Regions of Heart

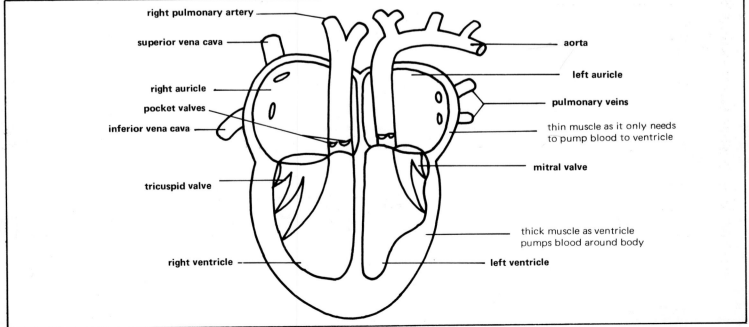

right pulmonary artery

aorta

superior vena cava

left auricle

right auricle

pulmonary veins

pocket valves

thin muscle as it only needs to pump blood to ventricle

inferior vena cava

mitral valve

tricuspid valve

thick muscle as ventricle pumps blood around body

right ventricle   **left ventricle**

Blood circulation

Action of Valves

These prevent blood flowing backwards:

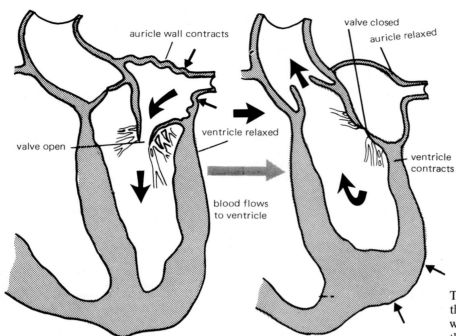

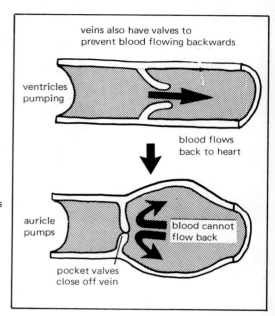

The heart therefore works like a pump and forces the blood around the body. Arteries have muscular walls to maintain the blood pressure but veins have thinner walls as little pressure is needed to return blood to the heart.

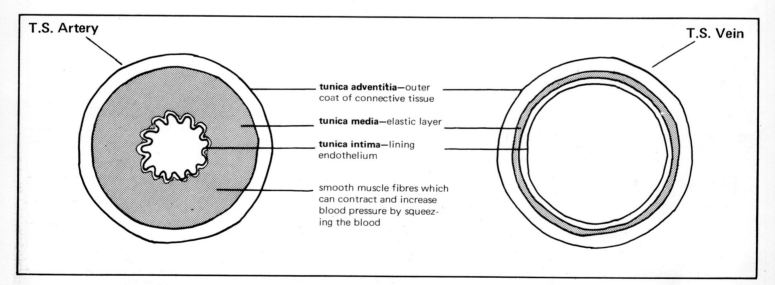

T.S. Artery

T.S. Vein

tunica adventitia—outer coat of connective tissue

tunica media—elastic layer

tunica intima—lining endothelium

smooth muscle fibres which can contract and increase blood pressure by squeezing the blood

When muscles of the skeleton contract they can help circulate blood by squeezing veins:

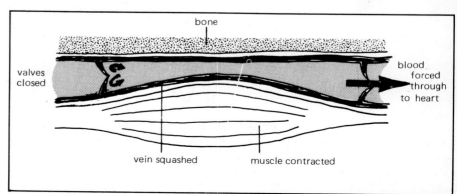

If this does not happen blood stagnates and may clot, causing thrombosis e.g. in legs.

The sphygmomanometer

This is used to measure the blood pressure in arteries.

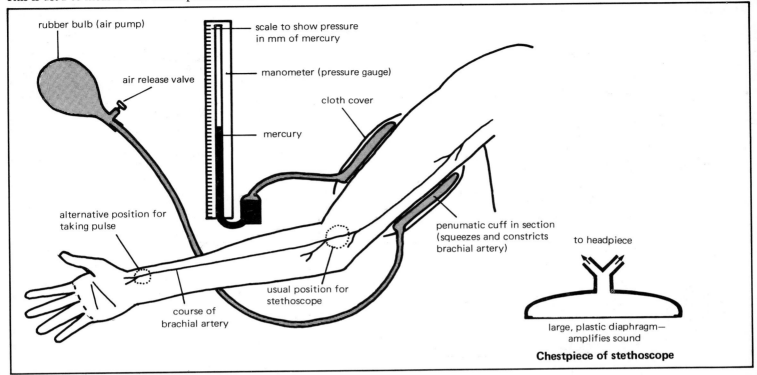

Chestpiece of stethoscope

Method of Use
1. Wrap pneumatic cuff firmly around upper arm
2. Place chestpiece of stethoscope lightly over brachial artery at bend of elbow
3. Increase pressure in cuff until pulse disappears
4. Open air release valve and slowly let pressure fall; listen to pulse:

average pressure	sound heard in stethoscope	systolic blood flow	
over 120 mm	no noise		no blood flow
120 mm	faint, short blowing sounds		artery just opens
	loud tapping		forced open wider
	murmer/blowing		slight constriction
75 mm	no noise		no constriction

systolic pressure →

diastolic pressure →

Systolic pressure minus diastolic pressure is the pulse pressure.

The pressure should be taken when the patient is relaxed in a warm room and before a meal. Cold, nervousness, digesting food, holding the breath and exercise all increase the blood pressure and therefore the amount of work the heart must do.

see also notes on heartbeat

Arteries and veins

Main Arteries

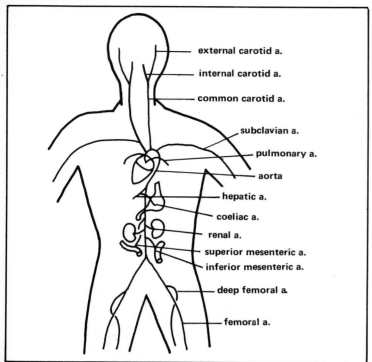

external carotid a.
internal carotid a.
common carotid a.
subclavian a.
pulmonary a.
aorta
hepatic a.
coeliac a.
renal a.
superior mesenteric a.
inferior mesenteric a.
deep femoral a.
femoral a.

Main Veins

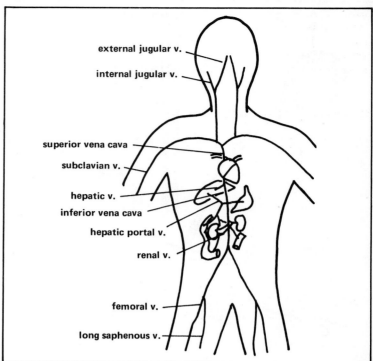

external jugular v.
internal jugular v.
superior vena cava
subclavian v.
hepatic v.
inferior vena cava
hepatic portal v.
renal v.
femoral v.
long saphenous v.

Diagram to Show Regulation of Heart Beat

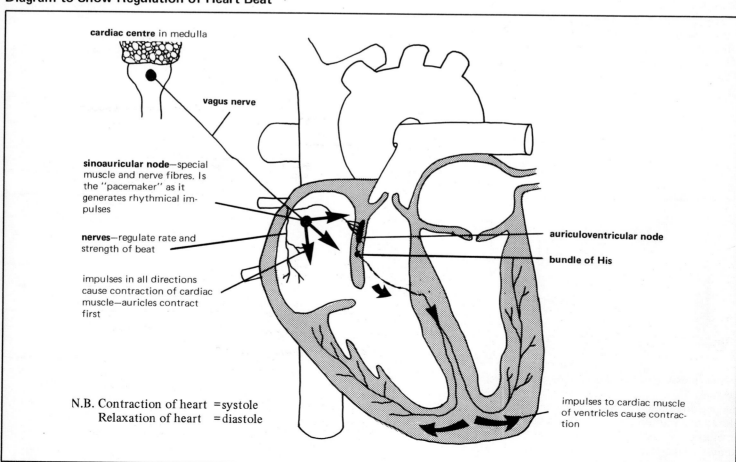

cardiac centre in medulla

vagus nerve

sinoauricular node—special muscle and nerve fibres. Is the "pacemaker" as it generates rhythmical impulses

nerves—regulate rate and strength of beat

impulses in all directions cause contraction of cardiac muscle—auricles contract first

auriculoventricular node

bundle of His

impulses to cardiac muscle of ventricles cause contraction

N.B. Contraction of heart = systole
Relaxation of heart = diastole

Common circulation/blood disorders

Abnormal heart beat:

a) **palpitations**—rapid, conscious beats—temporary
b) **tachycardia**—rapid, unconscious beats—permanent
c) **bradycardia**—slow beating
d) **extrasystoles**—extra, uneven beats
e) **atrial fibrillation**—palpitations of auricles (atria)

Hypertension—vessels, glands or kidneys compress blood—high pressure

c.a

s.a.

p.a.

Anaemia—less oxygen carrying capacity of blood:
a) Iron deficiency Anaemia—lack of iron so less haemoglobin made.
b) Pernicious Anaemia—lack of vitamin B_{12} (needed to make erythrocytes)

s.v.c.

i.v.c.

s.a.n.

a.v.n.

b. of H.

Heart block—Auriculoventricular node diseased

Mitral Stenosis—disordered valve

Mitral valve

Heart failure—ventricles do not empty fully (congential heart failure—both sides of heart affected)

t. valve

Jaundice—yellowing of blood as bile present. Due to blocked bile duct.

Blockage of Coronary artery:
a) Coronary thrombosis—complete block
b) Angina—partial block

Lymph

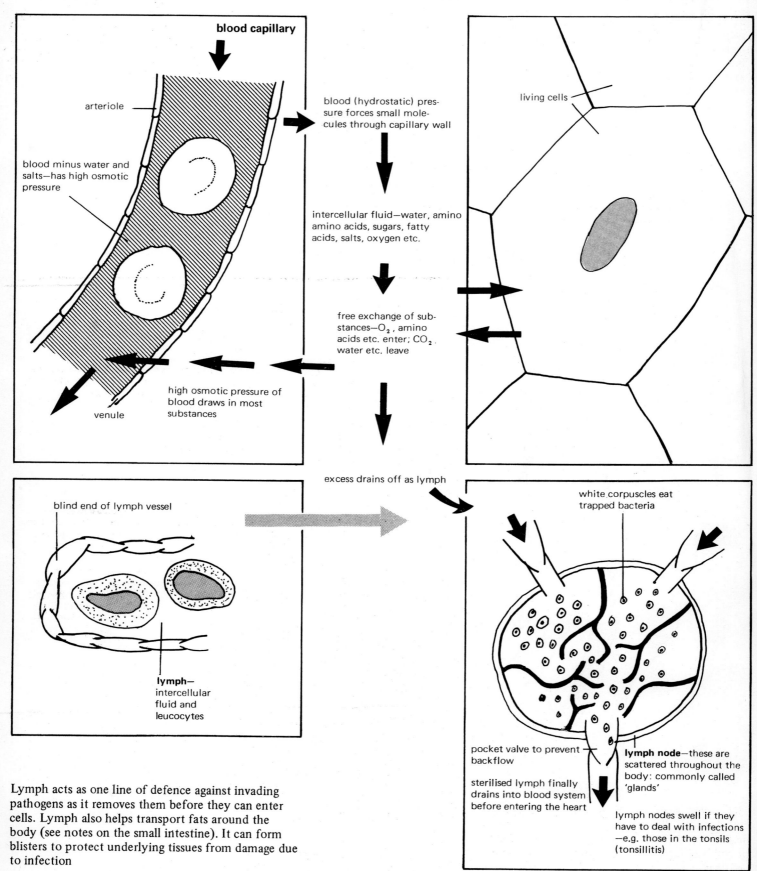

blood capillary

arteriole

blood minus water and salts—has high osmotic pressure

venule

blood (hydrostatic) pressure forces small molecules through capillary wall

intercellular fluid—water, amino amino acids, sugars, fatty acids, salts, oxygen etc.

free exchange of substances—O_2, amino acids etc. enter; CO_2, water etc. leave

high osmotic pressure of blood draws in most substances

living cells

excess drains off as lymph

blind end of lymph vessel

lymph—intercellular fluid and leucocytes

white corpuscles eat trapped bacteria

pocket valve to prevent backflow

sterilised lymph finally drains into blood system before entering the heart

lymph node—these are scattered throughout the body: commonly called 'glands'

lymph nodes swell if they have to deal with infections —e.g. those in the tonsils (tonsillitis)

Lymph acts as one line of defence against invading pathogens as it removes them before they can enter cells. Lymph also helps transport fats around the body (see notes on the small intestine). It can form blisters to protect underlying tissues from damage due to infection

Excretion

Definition

This is the name given to the process by which substances formed during metabolism i.e. the chemical reactions taking place within our cells, are removed from the body.

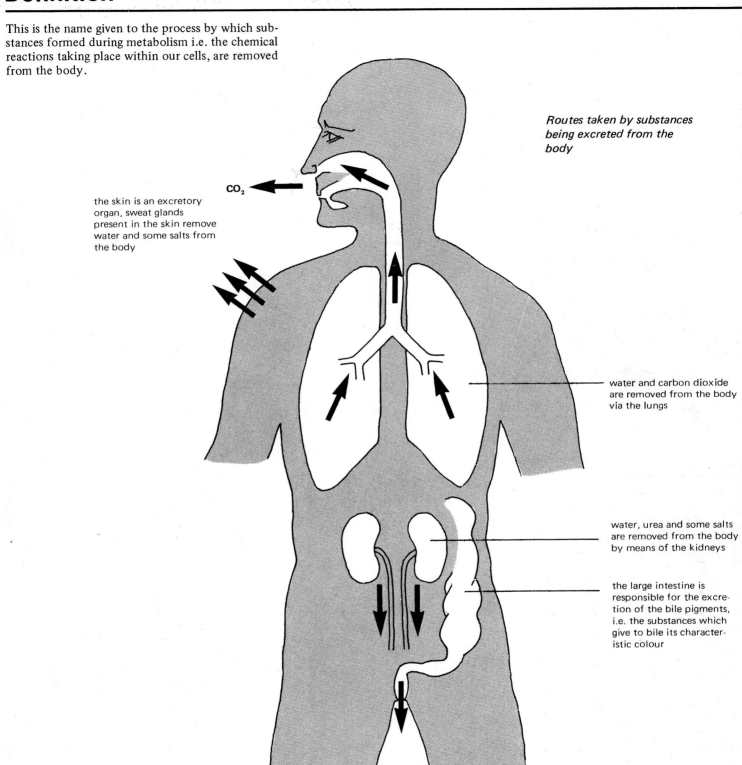

Routes taken by substances being excreted from the body

CO_2

the skin is an excretory organ, sweat glands present in the skin remove water and some salts from the body

water and carbon dioxide are removed from the body via the lungs

water, urea and some salts are removed from the body by means of the kidneys

the large intestine is responsible for the excretion of the bile pigments, i.e. the substances which give to bile its characteristic colour

The normal passing via the anus of substances which have not been digested and absorbed cannot be described as excretion as these substances are not products of metabolism. The process is known as defaecation.

The Urinary system

The Urinary System

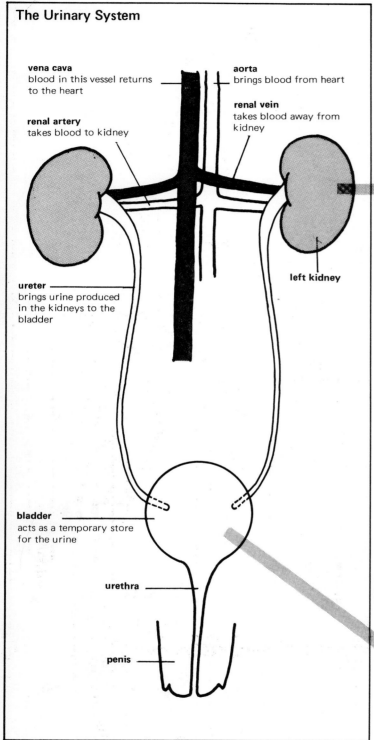

vena cava
blood in this vessel returns to the heart

aorta
brings blood from heart

renal vein
takes blood away from kidney

renal artery
takes blood to kidney

left kidney

ureter
brings urine produced in the kidneys to the bladder

bladder
acts as a temporary store for the urine

urethra

penis

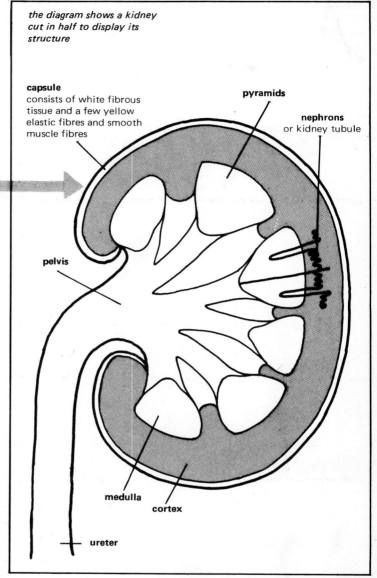

the diagram shows a kidney cut in half to display its structure

capsule
consists of white fibrous tissue and a few yellow elastic fibres and smooth muscle fibres

pyramids

nephrons
or kidney tubule

pelvis

medulla

cortex

ureter

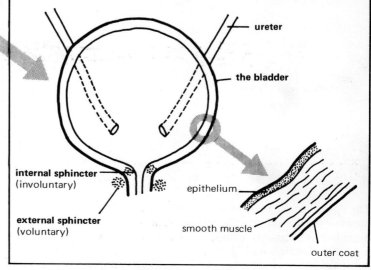

ureter

the bladder

internal sphincter
(involuntary)

external sphincter
(voluntary)

epithelium

smooth muscle

outer coat

Functions of the kidneys

1. The removal from the blood of urea, some water and some salts and their removal from the body as urine.

2. The maintaining of the salt-water balance of the tissue fluids.

The nephron or kidney tubule

A nephron
Each kidney contains about half a million nephrons

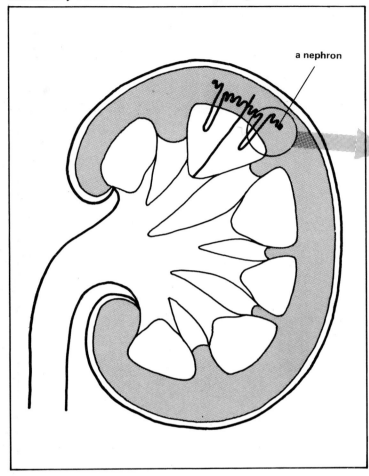

a nephron

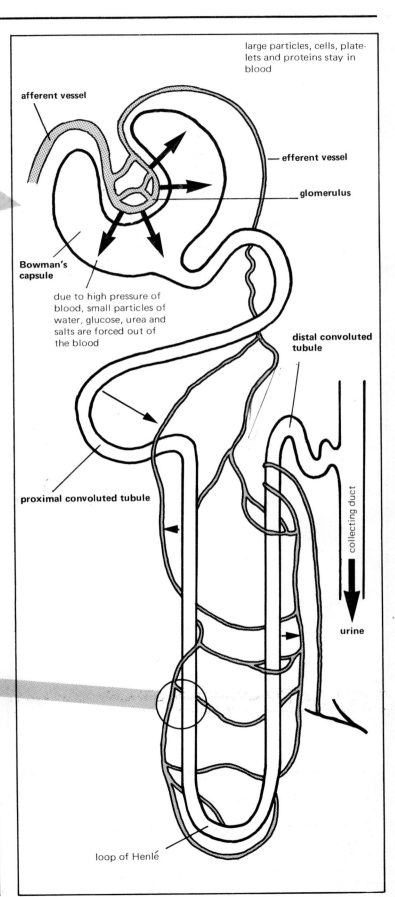

large particles, cells, platelets and proteins stay in blood

afferent vessel

efferent vessel

glomerulus

Bowman's capsule

due to high pressure of blood, small particles of water, glucose, urea and salts are forced out of the blood

distal convoluted tubule

proximal convoluted tubule

collecting duct

urine

loop of Henlé

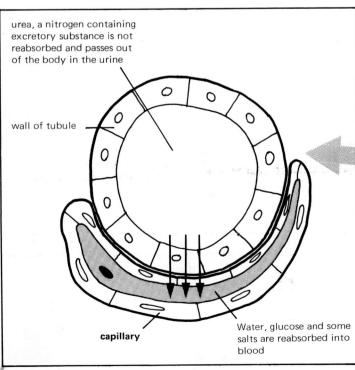

urea, a nitrogen containing excretory substance is not reabsorbed and passes out of the body in the urine

wall of tubule

capillary

Water, glucose and some salts are reabsorbed into blood

Excretion
The regulation of the water balance of the body

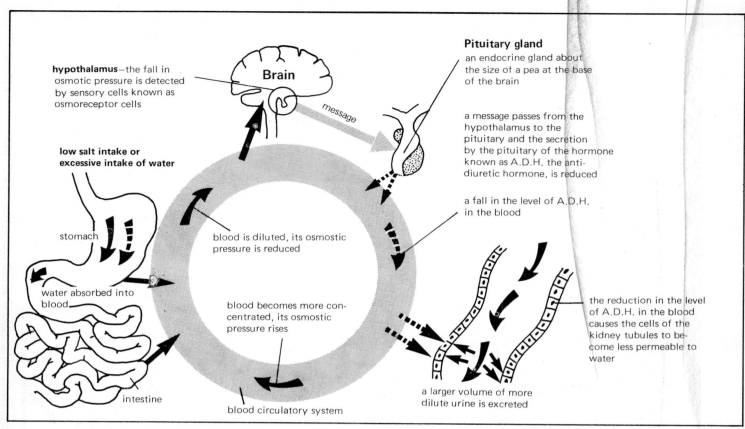

hypothalamus—the fall in osmotic pressure is detected by sensory cells known as osmoreceptor cells

Brain

message

Pituitary gland
an endocrine gland about the size of a pea at the base of the brain

a message passes from the hypothalamus to the pituitary and the secretion by the pituitary of the hormone known as A.D.H. the anti-diuretic hormone, is reduced

low salt intake or excessive intake of water

a fall in the level of A.D.H. in the blood

stomach

blood is diluted, its osmostic pressure is reduced

water absorbed into blood

blood becomes more concentrated, its osmostic pressure rises

the reduction in the level of A.D.H. in the blood causes the cells of the kidney tubules to become less permeable to water

intestine

blood circulatory system

a larger volume of more dilute urine is excreted

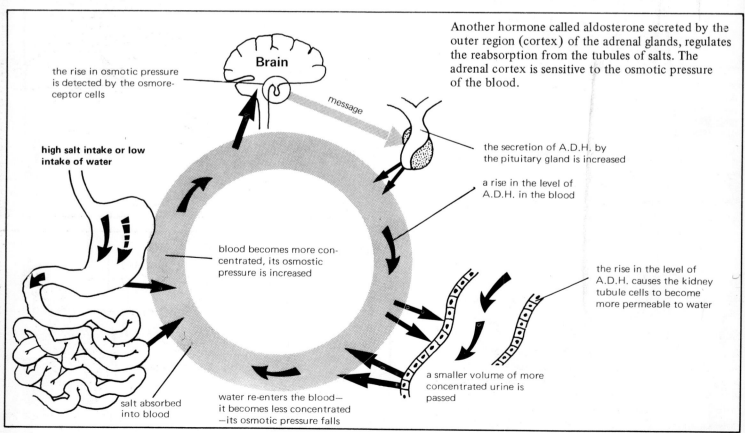

the rise in osmotic pressure is detected by the osmoreceptor cells

Brain

message

Another hormone called aldosterone secreted by the outer region (cortex) of the adrenal glands, regulates the reabsorption from the tubules of salts. The adrenal cortex is sensitive to the osmotic pressure of the blood.

the secretion of A.D.H. by the pituitary gland is increased

high salt intake or low intake of water

a rise in the level of A.D.H. in the blood

blood becomes more concentrated, its osmostic pressure is increased

the rise in the level of A.D.H. causes the kidney tubule cells to become more permeable to water

salt absorbed into blood

water re-enters the blood— it becomes less concentrated —its osmotic pressure falls

a smaller volume of more concentrated urine is passed

Co-ordination

The nervous system

This is the name given to the process whereby all body functions are regulated and controlled.

Two systems are concerned with co-ordination.

(1) The nervous system—consists of a series of fibres running to all parts of the body. Small electric currents called impulses pass along these fibres. One can liken the nervous system to a town's telephone service, the central nervous system being the telephone exchange, the peripheral nerves being like the lines leading from individual telephone receivers.

(2) The endocrine system

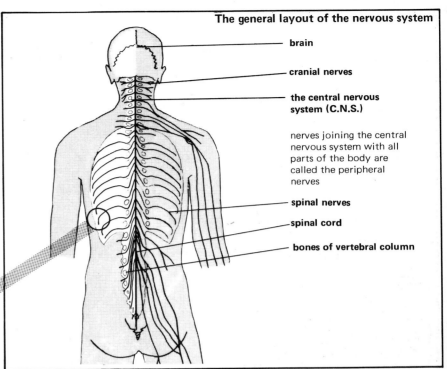

The general layout of the nervous system

- brain
- cranial nerves
- the central nervous system (C.N.S.)

nerves joining the central nervous system with all parts of the body are called the peripheral nerves

- spinal nerves
- spinal cord
- bones of vertebral column

A transverse section through a nerve

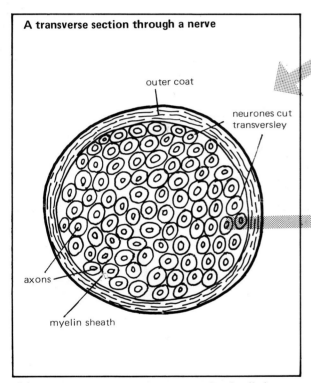

- outer coat
- neurones cut transversley
- axons
- myelin sheath

Nervous tissue consists of very specialised cells known as nerve cells or neurones. A nerve looks like a white thread and consists of a large number of neurones bounded by an outer coat.

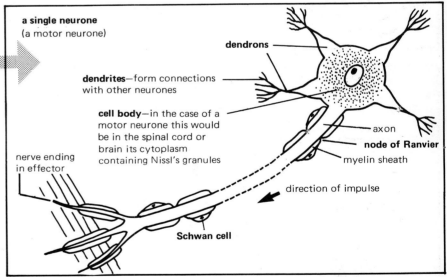

a single neurone (a motor neurone)

- **dendrons**
- **dendrites**—form connections with other neurones
- **cell body**—in the case of a motor neurone this would be in the spinal cord or brain its cytoplasm containing Nissl's granules
- nerve ending in effector
- axon
- **node of Ranvier**
- myelin sheath
- direction of impulse
- **Schwan cell**

Sensory receptor

These are cells which are able to detect changes in the person's surroundings, for example, the light sensitive cells in the retina of the eye, cells in the skin that are sensitive to touch, the taste buds of the tongue, cells in the lining of the nasal cavities responsible for the sense of smell and the cells of the organ of Corti in the inner ear.

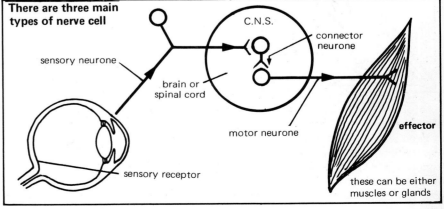

There are three main types of nerve cell

- C.N.S.
- connector neurone
- sensory neurone
- brain or spinal cord
- motor neurone
- sensory receptor
- **effector**
- these can be either muscles or glands

Reflexes

A reflex action is a very rapid response to a stimulus, that is independent of the will. For example: sneezing, coughing, vomiting, the later stages of swallowing, pulling the hand or foot away from a sharp object are all examples of reflex actions.

In a reflex action either the brain or the spinal cord may be involved. The diagram shows what is involved when saliva is produced on tasting food.

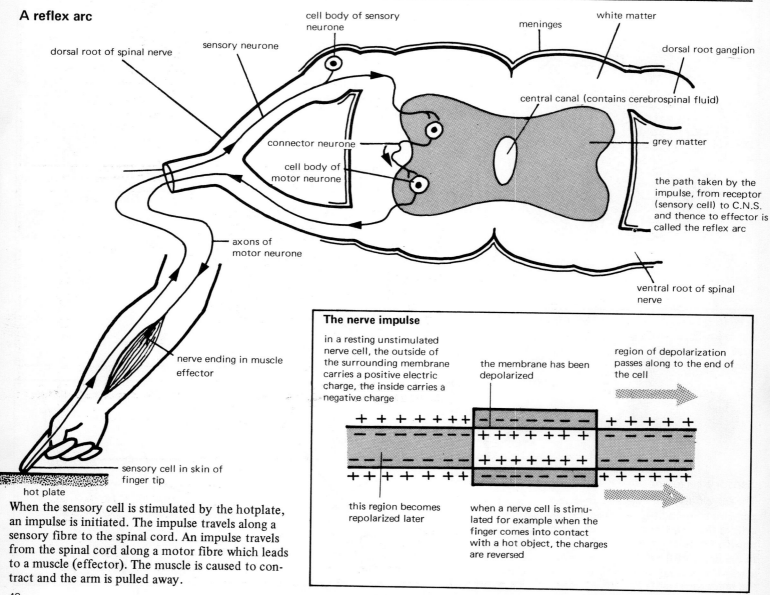

an impulse passes from the tongue to the medulla oblongata

brain

medulla oblongata

taste buds on tongue are stimulated by the food

an impulse passes along another neurone (a motor neurone) and causes the salivary gland to secrete more saliva

salivary gland

A reflex arc

dorsal root of spinal nerve

sensory neurone

cell body of sensory neurone

meninges

white matter

dorsal root ganglion

central canal (contains cerebrospinal fluid)

connector neurone

cell body of motor neurone

grey matter

the path taken by the impulse, from receptor (sensory cell) to C.N.S. and thence to effector is called the reflex arc

axons of motor neurone

ventral root of spinal nerve

nerve ending in muscle effector

sensory cell in skin of finger tip

hot plate

When the sensory cell is stimulated by the hotplate, an impulse is initiated. The impulse travels along a sensory fibre to the spinal cord. An impulse travels from the spinal cord along a motor fibre which leads to a muscle (effector). The muscle is caused to contract and the arm is pulled away.

The nerve impulse

in a resting unstimulated nerve cell, the outside of the surrounding membrane carries a positive electric charge, the inside carries a negative charge

the membrane has been depolarized

region of depolarization passes along to the end of the cell

this region becomes repolarized later

when a nerve cell is stimulated for example when the finger comes into contact with a hot object, the charges are reversed

The brain

The brain is the main co-ordinating centre of the nervous system, it is also concerned with memory, reasoning, creative judgement and consciousness.

The brain from above.

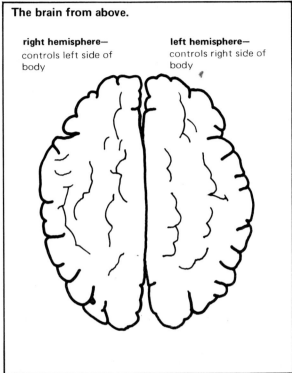

right hemisphere— controls left side of body

left hemisphere— controls right side of body

Side view of the brain.

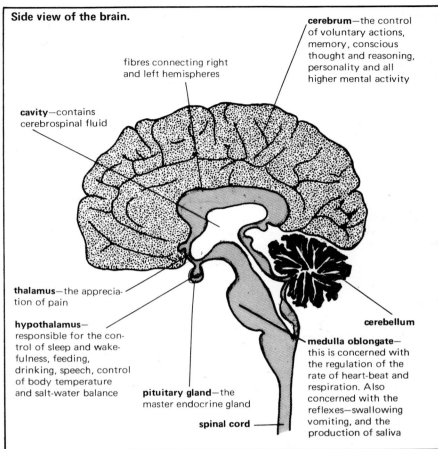

fibres connecting right and left hemispheres

cerebrum—the control of voluntary actions, memory, conscious thought and reasoning, personality and all higher mental activity

cavity—contains cerebrospinal fluid

thalamus—the appreciation of pain

hypothalamus— responsible for the control of sleep and wakefulness, feeding, drinking, speech, control of body temperature and salt-water balance

pituitary gland—the master endocrine gland

spinal cord

cerebellum

medulla oblongate— this is concerned with the regulation of the rate of heart-beat and respiration. Also concerned with the reflexes—swallowing vomiting, and the production of saliva

This diagram shows some tissue from the cerebral cortex as it would appear under the microscope

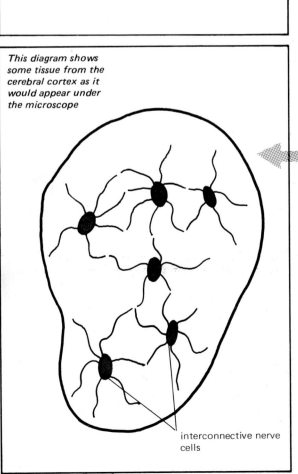

interconnective nerve cells

Section through part of the cerebrum

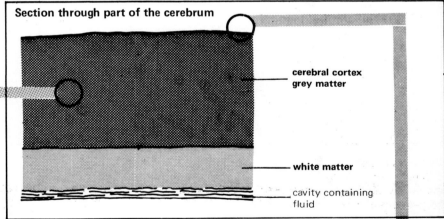

cerebral cortex grey matter

white matter

cavity containing fluid

The brain and spinal cord are surrounded by three membranes known as the meninges. Their function is to protect the brain.

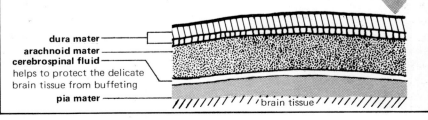

dura mater
arachnoid mater
cerebrospinal fluid
helps to protect the delicate brain tissue from buffeting
pia mater

brain tissue

The brain

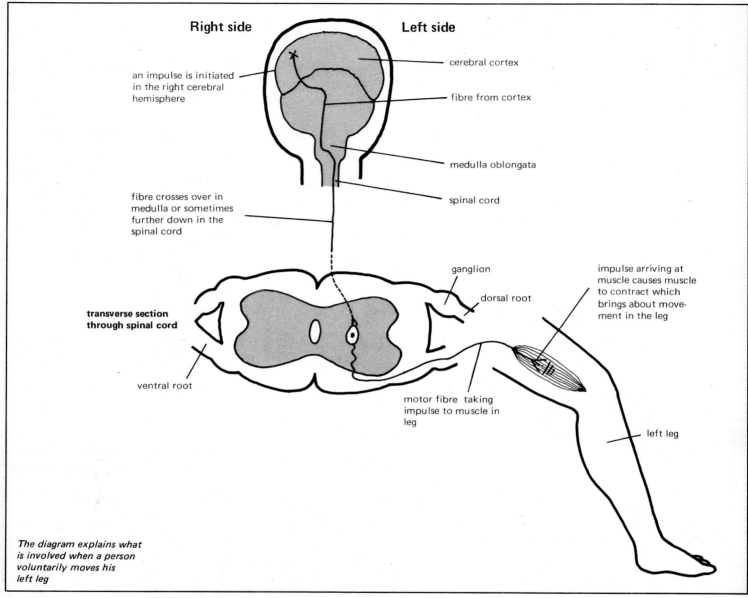

Right side   Left side

cerebral cortex

an impulse is initiated
in the right cerebral
hemisphere

fibre from cortex

medulla oblongata

spinal cord

fibre crosses over in
medulla or sometimes
further down in the
spinal cord

ganglion

dorsal root

impulse arriving at
muscle causes muscle
to contract which
brings about move-
ment in the leg

**transverse section
through spinal cord**

ventral root

motor fibre taking
impulse to muscle in
leg

left leg

*The diagram explains what
is involved when a person
voluntarily moves his
left leg*

By means of applying minute electric currents to
different parts of the brain it has been possible to
discover which parts of the brain control many
body functions.

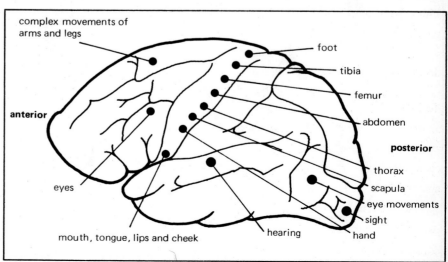

complex movements of
arms and legs

foot

tibia

femur

abdomen

anterior

posterior

thorax

scapula

eye movements

sight

eyes

hand

mouth, tongue, lips and cheek

hearing

The autonomic nervous system

This is that part of the nervous system concerned with the control of the parts of the body not under the control of the will.

Brain

The parasympathetic nervous system

The sympathetic nervous system

Prepares the body for action—stimulated in times of danger or anger

These structures are not under control of the will. You cannot consciously alter the speed of your heart beat or decrease the contractions of involuntary muscle in the wall of your stomach

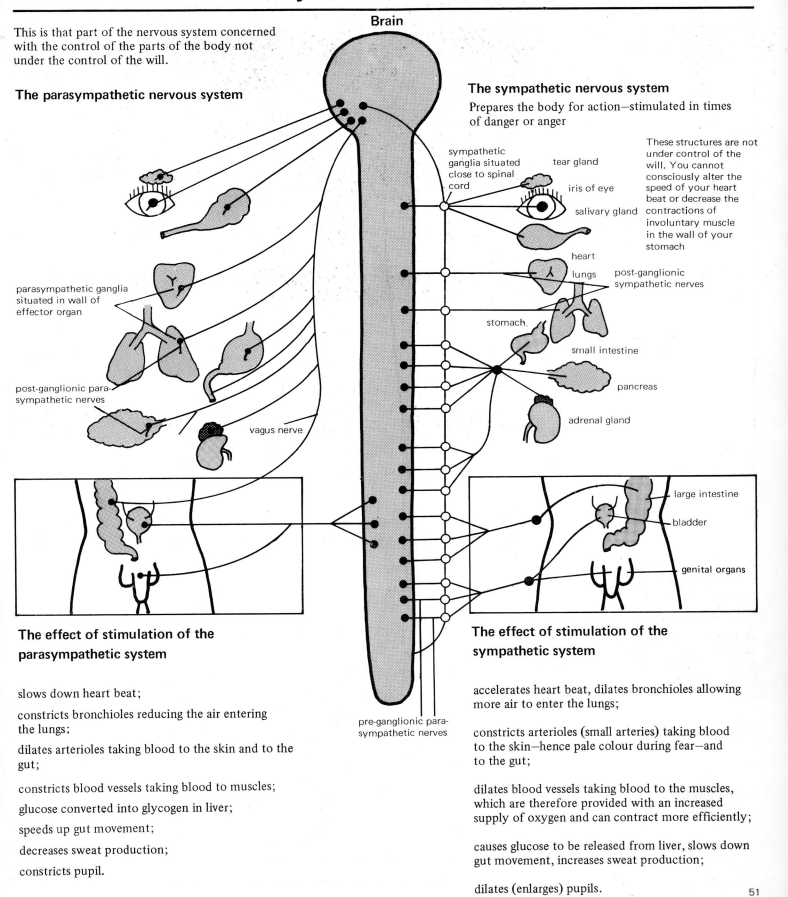

sympathetic ganglia situated close to spinal cord

tear gland

iris of eye

salivary gland

heart

lungs

post-ganglionic sympathetic nerves

parasympathetic ganglia situated in wall of effector organ

stomach,

small intestine

pancreas

post-ganglionic para-sympathetic nerves

adrenal gland

vagus nerve

large intestine

bladder

genital organs

pre-ganglionic para-sympathetic nerves

The effect of stimulation of the parasympathetic system

slows down heart beat;

constricts bronchioles reducing the air entering the lungs;

dilates arterioles taking blood to the skin and to the gut;

constricts blood vessels taking blood to muscles;

glucose converted into glycogen in liver;

speeds up gut movement;

decreases sweat production;

constricts pupil.

The effect of stimulation of the sympathetic system

accelerates heart beat, dilates bronchioles allowing more air to enter the lungs;

constricts arterioles (small arteries) taking blood to the skin—hence pale colour during fear—and to the gut;

dilates blood vessels taking blood to the muscles, which are therefore provided with an increased supply of oxygen and can contract more efficiently;

causes glucose to be released from liver, slows down gut movement, increases sweat production;

dilates (enlarges) pupils.

The endocrine system

The second system of the body concerned with co-ordination

All endocrine glands are very vascular, i.e. well supplied with blood vessels—the hormones which the glands produce pass directly into the blood

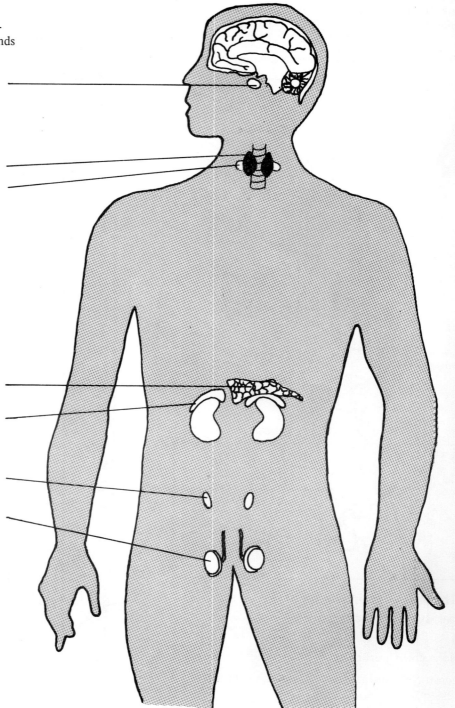

pituitary gland— thyrotrophic hormones, gonadotrophic hormones, adrenocortico-trophic hormones, prolactin, growth hormones, oxytocin, vasopressin

thyroid gland—thyroxine

parathyroid gland— parathormone

pancreas—islets of Langerhans—insulin

adrenal gland—adrenaline cortisone, hydro-cortisone, aldosterone

ovary (in female) oestrogen, progesterone

testis (in male)— testosterone

The endocrine system consists of a series of glands which produce and secrete directly into the blood substances known as hormones.

Hormones act as chemical messengers. They travel around the body in the blood, having an effect on certain cells or tissues far from where they were produced. Note that unlike the secretions of the salivary glands and sweat glands, hormones do not travel along tubes or ducts to reach their place of action; the endocrine glands are therefore often known as the ductless glands.

The nervous system and endocrine system compared

Nervous system

Message in form of electric current (impulse). Message travels along a nerve fibre—part of neurone. One nerve fibre usually affects only one muscle or gland cell. Nervous system controls quick acting, short lasting actions, for example, drawing of foot away from pin.

Endocrine system

Message in form of a chemical (hormone). Message travels around body in the blood. A hormone can affect many cells through the body. Endocrine system regulates the more long lasting processes taking place within the body, for example, metabolic rate.

The pituitary gland

This gland, about the size of a pea, is located at the base of the brain. Because the hormones it secretes have a regulating effect on the other endocrine glands, it is often known as the master gland.

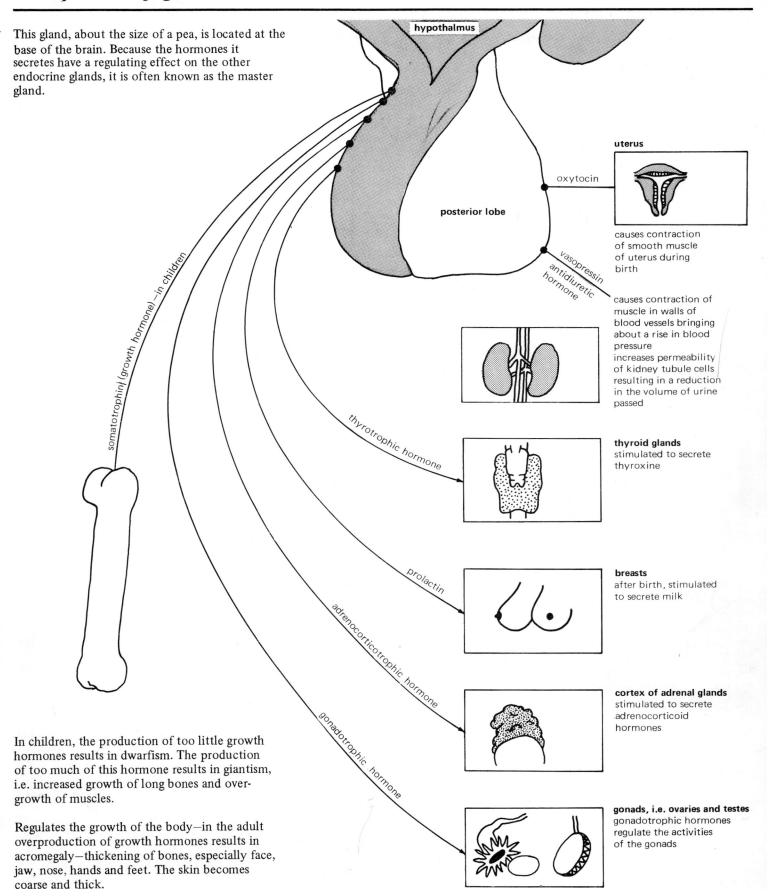

hypothalmus

posterior lobe

oxytocin

uterus

causes contraction of smooth muscle of uterus during birth

vasopressin antidiuretic hormone

causes contraction of muscle in walls of blood vessels bringing about a rise in blood pressure
increases permeability of kidney tubule cells resulting in a reduction in the volume of urine passed

thyrotrophic hormone

thyroid glands
stimulated to secrete thyroxine

somatotrophin (growth hormone) — in children

prolactin

breasts
after birth, stimulated to secrete milk

adrenocorticotrophic hormone

cortex of adrenal glands
stimulated to secrete adrenocorticoid hormones

gonadotrophic hormone

gonads, i.e. ovaries and testes
gonadotrophic hormones regulate the activities of the gonads

In children, the production of too little growth hormones results in dwarfism. The production of too much of this hormone results in giantism, i.e. increased growth of long bones and over-growth of muscles.

Regulates the growth of the body—in the adult overproduction of growth hormones results in acromegaly—thickening of bones, especially face, jaw, nose, hands and feet. The skin becomes coarse and thick.

The pituitary gland

The very tall man is suffering from hyperpituitarism, too much growth hormone was secreted by his pituitary gland during childhood.

The very small man suffers from hypopituitarism, his pituitary gland did not secrete sufficient growth hormone during childhood.

This woman is suffering from acromegaly. This occurs when the pituitary gland is overactive in adult life. When the pituitary gland secretes too much growth hormone in the adult, the bones of the hands and feet and jaws become excessively developed and the skin becomes coarse.

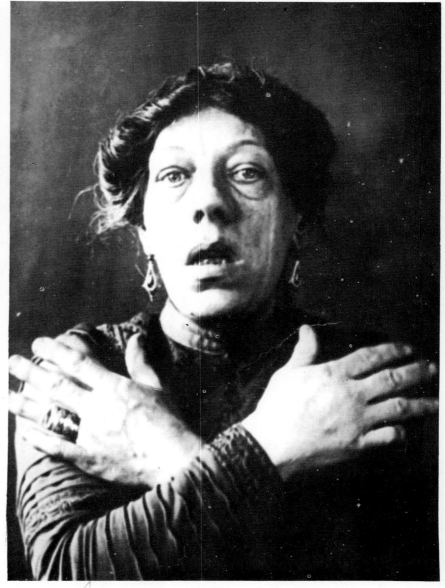

The thyroid and parathyroid glands

Thyroid gland

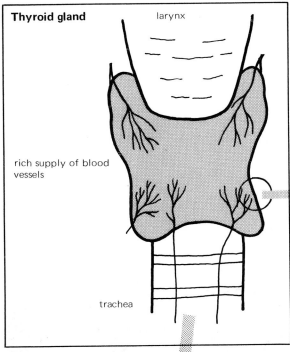

larynx

rich supply of blood vessels

trachea

blood capillary

iodine from blood

linked with a protein to form thyroglobulin

thyroxine

thyroxine passes into blood when required

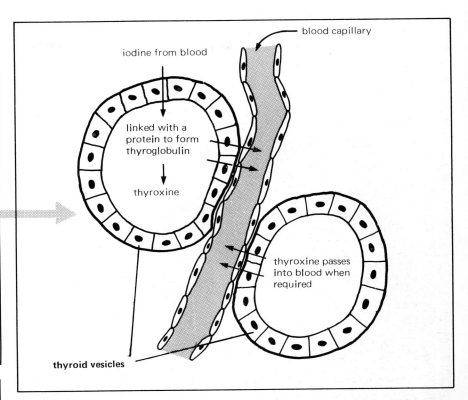

thyroid vesicles

Parathyroid glands

overproduction of parathormone—rise in blood calcium, a gradual softening and deformity of bone

underproduction of parathormone—great decrease in blood calcium, twitchings, nervousness, spasms of face and limb muscles; this condition is known as tetany

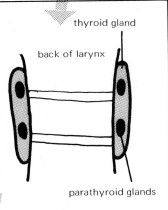

thyroid gland

back of larynx

parathyroid glands

as level of calcium and phosphorous in blood falls para-thormone secreted by parathyroid glands

increased calcium and phosphorus decreases secretion of hormone

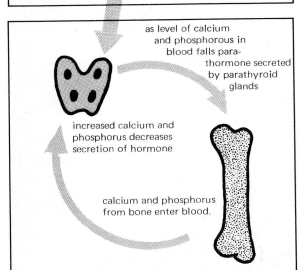

calcium and phosphorus from bone enter blood.

Hormonal control

pituitary gland

as level of thyroxine in blood falls, the pituitary secretes more thyrotrophic hormone

thyroxine released into blood

as level of thyroxine in blood increases, the amount of thyrotrophic hormone secreted by the pituitary is reduced

thyrotrophic hormone stimulates the thyroid gland to secrete thyroxine

body tissues

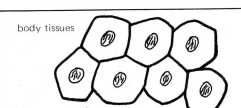

thyroxine acts as a catalyst speeding up the process of respiration

The thyroid gland

This patient suffers from thyrotoxicosis or hyperthyroidism, her thyroid gland is enlarged and is producing too much thyroxine.

Note the swelling in the neck and bulging eyes.

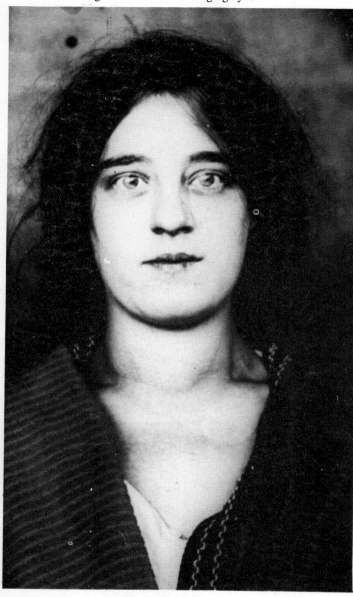

In the photograph below the patient suffers from Myxoedema. Her thyroid gland is underactive producing too little thyroxine.

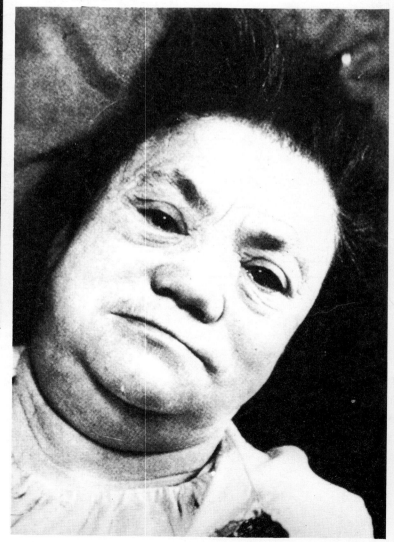

The thyroid gland

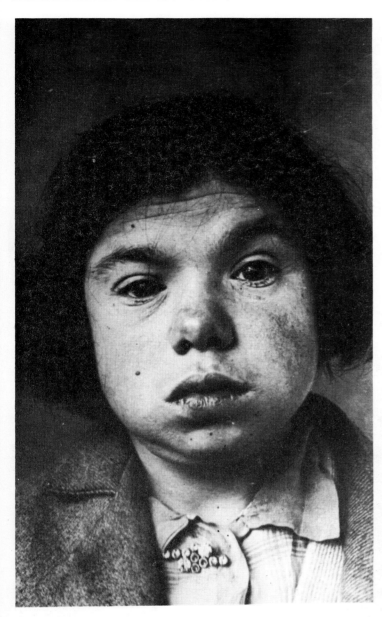

The photograph above shows a patient suffering from cretinism the condition in which too little thyroxine is produced during childhood. On the right we see the same woman after treatment with thyroxine.

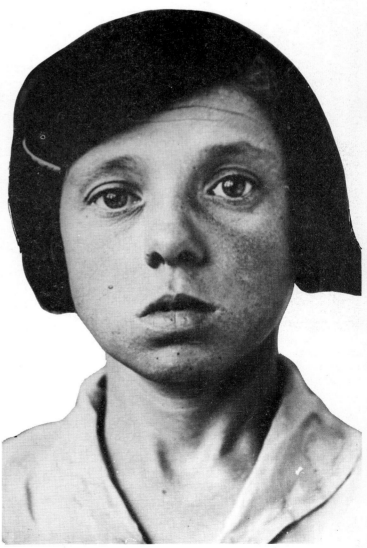

The pancreas as an endocrine gland

The pancreas contains the Islets of Langerhans, which control the amount of glucose in the blood.

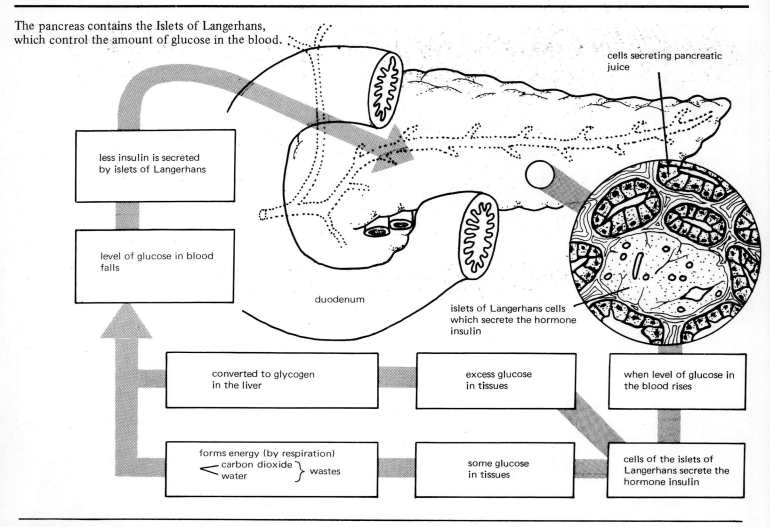

cells secreting pancreatic juice

less insulin is secreted by islets of Langerhans

level of glucose in blood falls

duodenum

islets of Langerhans cells which secrete the hormone insulin

converted to glycogen in the liver

excess glucose in tissues

when level of glucose in the blood rises

forms energy (by respiration) < carbon dioxide / water } wastes

some glucose in tissues

cells of the islets of Langerhans secrete the hormone insulin

---

If too little insulin is secreted by the islets of Langerhans, the person suffers from the disease called diabetes mellitus, the symptoms of which are (1) glucose present in the urine, (2) thirst, (3) general weakness, (4) loss of weight, (5) finally coma followed by death.

Diabetes can be controlled by means of regular injections of insulin together with regular meals.

If a meal is missed and insulin is injected, the level of glucose in the blood will fall and the patient may lose consciousness. This is called hypoglycaemia.

If the diabetic eats a large carboydrate rich meal and misses an injection of insulin, the level of glucose in the blood will rise to a dangerous level. A diabetic coma may result.

Carbohydrate intake must be balanced against insulin injected so that the level of glucose in the blood becomes neither too high nor too low.

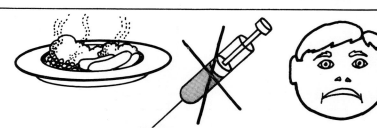

The adrenal gland

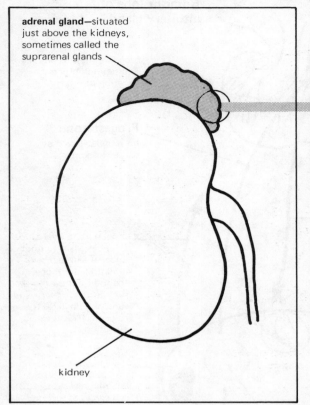

adrenal gland—situated just above the kidneys, sometimes called the suprarenal glands

kidney

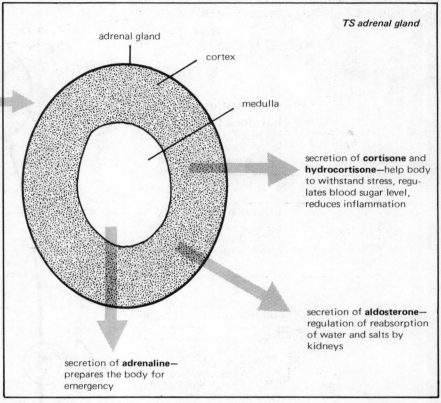

TS adrenal gland

adrenal gland

cortex

medulla

secretion of **cortisone** and **hydrocortisone**—help body to withstand stress, regulates blood sugar level, reduces inflammation

secretion of **aldosterone**—regulation of reabsorption of water and salts by kidneys

secretion of **adrenaline**—prepares the body for emergency

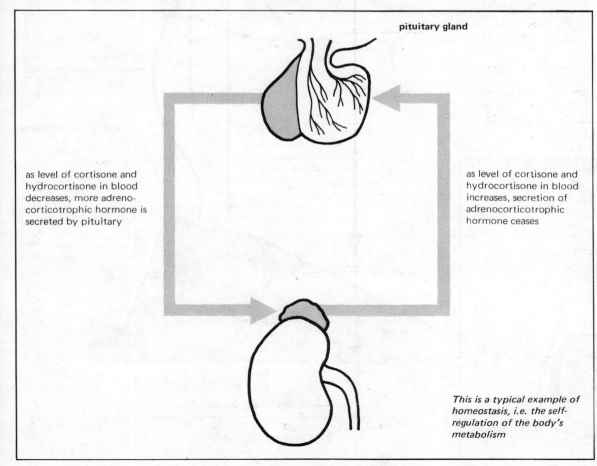

pituitary gland

as level of cortisone and hydrocortisone in blood decreases, more adrenocorticotrophic hormone is secreted by pituitary

as level of cortisone and hydrocortisone in blood increases, secretion of adrenocorticotrophic hormone ceases

This is a typical example of homeostasis, i.e. the self-regulation of the body's metabolism

The hormonal control of the reproductive system

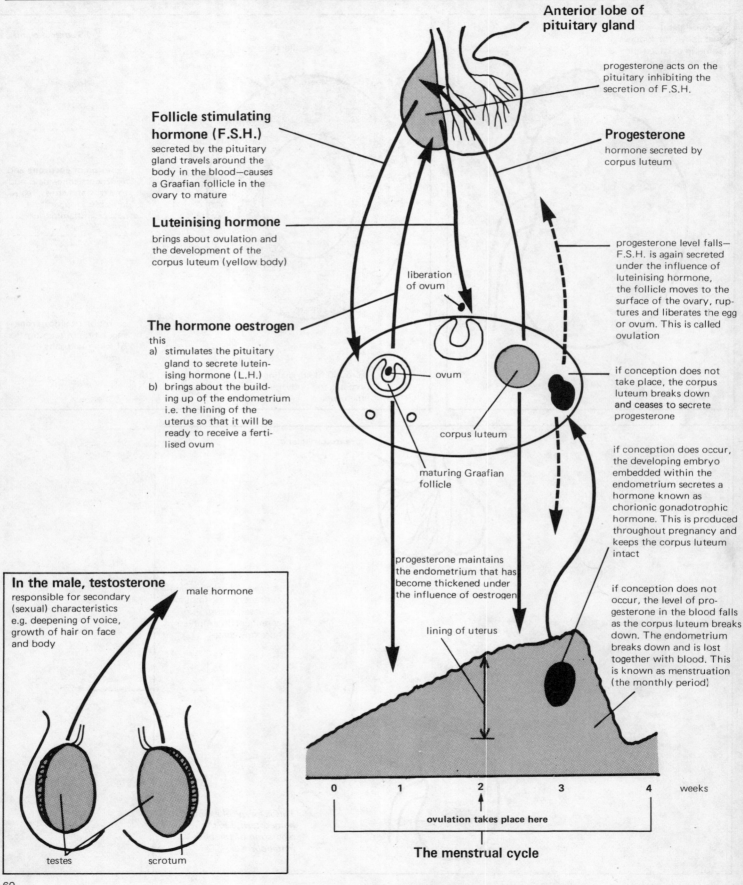

Anterior lobe of pituitary gland

progesterone acts on the pituitary inhibiting the secretion of F.S.H.

Follicle stimulating hormone (F.S.H.)
secreted by the pituitary gland travels around the body in the blood—causes a Graafian follicle in the ovary to mature

Progesterone
hormone secreted by corpus luteum

Luteinising hormone
brings about ovulation and the development of the corpus luteum (yellow body)

progesterone level falls— F.S.H. is again secreted under the influence of luteinising hormone, the follicle moves to the surface of the ovary, ruptures and liberates the egg or ovum. This is called ovulation

liberation of ovum

The hormone oestrogen
this
a) stimulates the pituitary gland to secrete luteinising hormone (L.H.)
b) brings about the building up of the endometrium i.e. the lining of the uterus so that it will be ready to receive a fertilised ovum

ovum

if conception does not take place, the corpus luteum breaks down and ceases to secrete progesterone

corpus luteum

maturing Graafian follicle

if conception does occur, the developing embryo embedded within the endometrium secretes a hormone known as chorionic gonadotrophic hormone. This is produced throughout pregnancy and keeps the corpus luteum intact

In the male, testosterone
responsible for secondary (sexual) characteristics e.g. deepening of voice, growth of hair on face and body

male hormone

progesterone maintains the endometrium that has become thickened under the influence of oestrogen

if conception does not occur, the level of progesterone in the blood falls as the corpus luteum breaks down. The endometrium breaks down and is lost together with blood. This is known as menstruation (the monthly period)

lining of uterus

testes   scrotum

0   1   2   3   4   weeks

ovulation takes place here

The menstrual cycle

Senses and sense organs

The eye

All sense cells work by stopping the energy of a stimulus and converting it to the nervous energy of an impulse. Different sense organs are special-lised for dealing with different forms of energy:

light energy → eye → impulses
sound energy → ear → impulses
chemical energy → tongue and nose → impulses
Mechanical energy → skin receptors and
　　　　　　　　proprioceptors → impulses

The brain interprets the impulses from the sense organs as vision, hearing, taste, smell, touch and muscle tone.

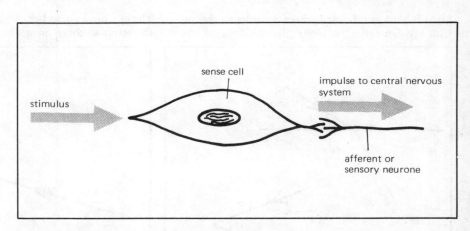

sense cell

stimulus

impulse to central nervous system

afferent or sensory neurone

The eye

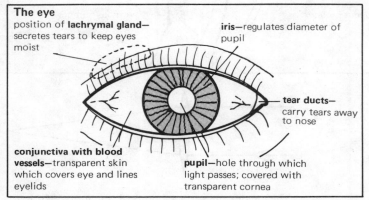

position of **lachrymal gland**—secretes tears to keep eyes moist

iris—regulates diameter of pupil

tear ducts—carry tears away to nose

conjunctiva with blood vessels—transparent skin which covers eye and lines eyelids

pupil—hole through which light passes; covered with transparent cornea

Field of vision of right eye looking forwards

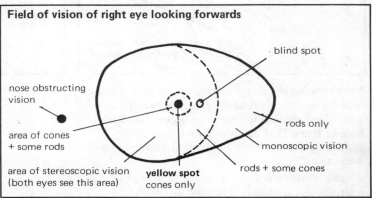

blind spot

nose obstructing vision

area of cones + some rods

area of stereoscopic vision (both eyes see this area)

yellow spot cones only

rods only

monoscopic vision

rods + some cones

Horizontal t.s. of right eye

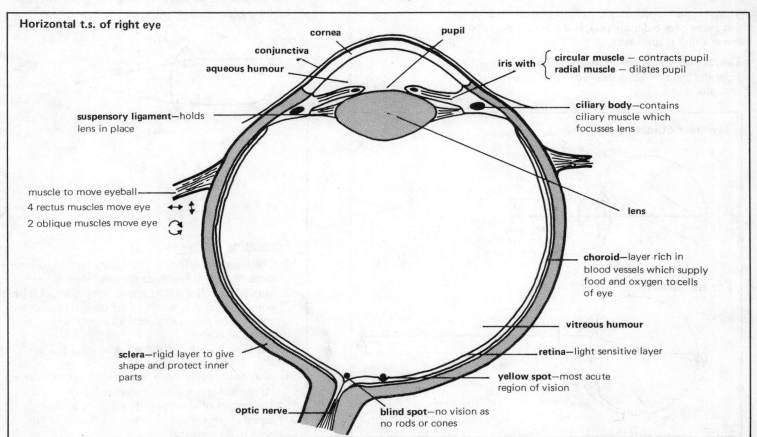

cornea

pupil

conjunctiva

aqueous humour

iris with { **circular muscle** — contracts pupil
radial muscle — dilates pupil

suspensory ligament—holds lens in place

ciliary body—contains ciliary muscle which focusses lens

muscle to move eyeball
4 rectus muscles move eye
2 oblique muscles move eye

lens

choroid—layer rich in blood vessels which supply food and oxygen to cells of eye

vitreous humour

sclera—rigid layer to give shape and protect inner parts

retina—light sensitive layer

yellow spot—most acute region of vision

optic nerve

blind spot—no vision as no rods or cones

Focussing light

Light is bent or refracted where it enters a substance with a higher refractive index (like density)

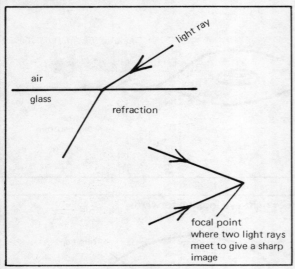

air
glass
light ray
refraction

focal point where two light rays meet to give a sharp image

The eye must focus light rays onto rods and cones of the retina so sharp images are formed:

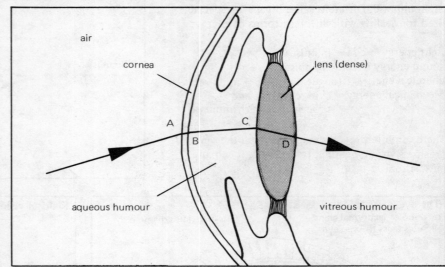

air
cornea
lens (dense)
A
B
C
D
aqueous humour
vitreous humour

Most focusing or refraction takes place at A because here there is the greatest difference between refractive indices. More focusing occurs at C but little at B and D as the refractive indices of the cornea/aqueuos humour and lens/vitreous humour are similar.

Accommodation is the term given to the eye's ability to focus objects at various distances.

The near point, (about 90mm for a person aged 20 but greater for older people), is the closest point to the eye that it can focus.

The far point (about 6 metres) is the farthest point from the eye that the lens needs to focus an object onto the retina.

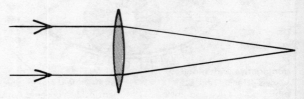

The greater the surface is curved, the more light is bent by a lens.

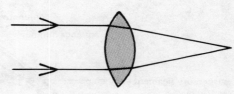

For near objects

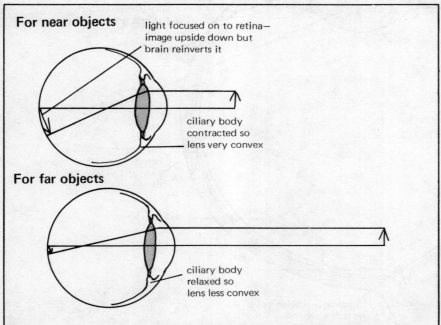

light focused on to retina— image upside down but brain reinverts it

ciliary body contracted so lens very convex

For far objects

ciliary body relaxed so lens less convex

Estimating distances

1. The muscular effort by the ciliary muscle to accommodate the eye is greater for near objects.
2. Muscles attached to the sclera must contract more to point both eyes towards a near object, (binocular vision), less for a far object. The brain senses all muscular effort.
3. Far objects look blurred when looking at near objects and vice-versa.
4. Near objects give sharp images with bright colours; far objects give indistinct shapes and dull colours.
5. The images of close objects are from different aspects for each eye (3-D vision). Those of far objects are similar.

Vision and defects of the eye

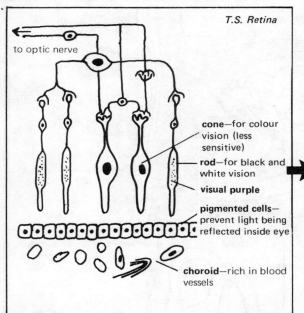

T.S. Retina

to optic nerve

cone—for colour vision (less sensitive)

rod—for black and white vision

visual purple

pigmented cells—prevent light being reflected inside eye

choroid—rich in blood vessels

Rods and cones contain light-sensitive pigments (called visual purple in rods) which are responsible for generating the nerve impulses in the optic nerve fibres:

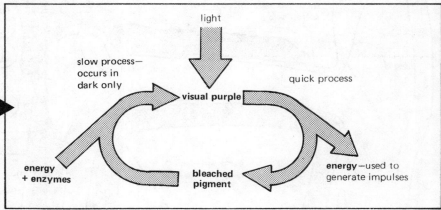

light

slow process—occurs in dark only

quick process

visual purple

energy + enzymes

bleached pigment

energy—used to generate impulses

The brain interprets the impulses as vision. Optical illusions occur when it misinterprets the impulses e.g.

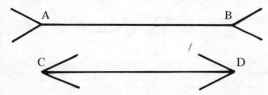

The lines AB and CD are the same length—the eyes faithfully record this but the brain is confused by the ends.

Focusing defects

1. Long sight (hypermetropia).
   Person cannot see close objects clearly.

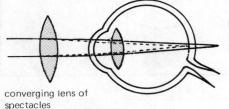

before spectacles worn, image focussed behind retina

converging lens of spectacles

The lens gradually loses its elasticity so elderly people are usually long-sighted (called presbyopia) and need spectacles for reading etc.

2. Short sight (myopia).
   Person cannot see far objects clearly.

diverging, concave spectacles

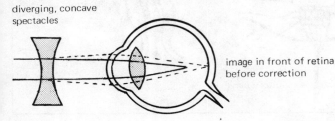

image in front of retina before correction

Defects of the eye

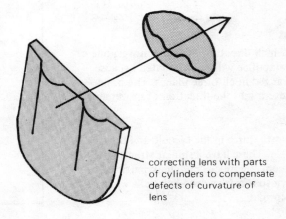

ulceration of the cornea—cured by corneal graft from donated eye

cataract (opaque lens)—lens removed and replace with plastic one

detached retina—welded into place using laser beams

glaucoma—pressure in vitreous humour too great and may destroy rods and cones—cured by drugs or operation to remove some fluid

colour blindness—sex-linked malfunction of cones. No cure

3. Astigmatism.
   The lens is distorted causing an uneven image to be focussed onto the retina.

correcting lens with parts of cylinders to compensate defects of curvature of lens

The ear

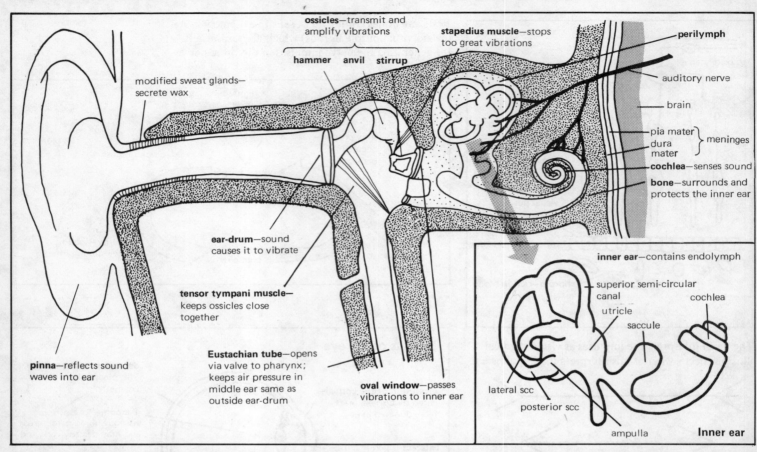

ossicles—transmit and amplify vibrations

hammer anvil stirrup

stapedius muscle—stops too great vibrations

perilymph

auditory nerve

brain

modified sweat glands—secrete wax

pia mater
dura mater } meninges

cochlea—senses sound

bone—surrounds and protects the inner ear

ear-drum—sound causes it to vibrate

tensor tympani muscle—keeps ossicles close together

pinna—reflects sound waves into ear

Eustachian tube—opens via valve to pharynx; keeps air pressure in middle ear same as outside ear-drum

oval window—passes vibrations to inner ear

inner ear—contains endolymph

superior semi-circular canal

cochlea

utricle

saccule

lateral scc

posterior scc

ampulla

Inner ear

Hearing

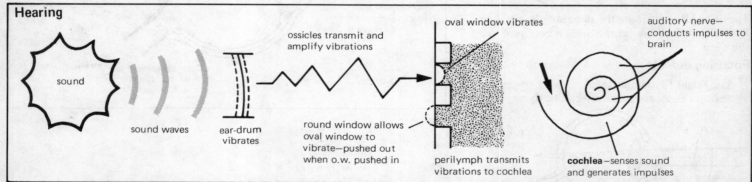

sound

sound waves

ear-drum vibrates

ossicles transmit and amplify vibrations

oval window vibrates

round window allows oval window to vibrate—pushed out when o.w. pushed in

perilymph transmits vibrations to cochlea

auditory nerve—conducts impulses to brain

cochlea—senses sound and generates impulses

The ear senses movements and balance as well as sound:—

Movement

No matter which direction the head moves, one or two of the ampullae will be stimulated because they are arranged in all three planes. The brain therefore determines the direction of movement.

Balance

Detected by structures in the saccule and utricle called maculae. These have a similar structure to ampullae except the mucus has chalk particles to make it heavy so it settles onto hair cells when the head is upright.

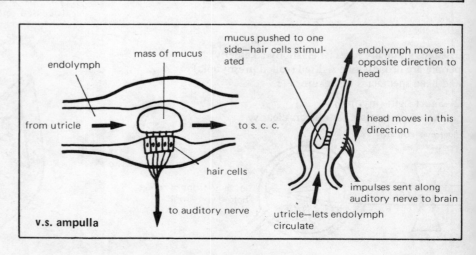

endolymph

mass of mucus

mucus pushed to one side—hair cells stimulated

endolymph moves in opposite direction to head

from utricle

to s. c. c.

head moves in this direction

hair cells

to auditory nerve

impulses sent along auditory nerve to brain

utricle—lets endolymph circulate

v.s. ampulla

The ear (continued) and Touch

T.S. organ of Corti in cochlea

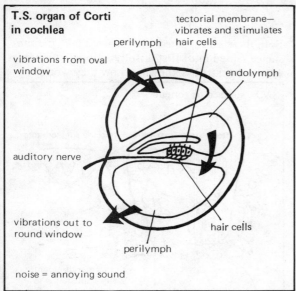

tectorial membrane—vibrates and stimulates hair cells

perilymph

vibrations from oval window

endolymph

auditory nerve

vibrations out to round window

hair cells

perilymph

noise = annoying sound

sound intensity—determined as loud sounds generate more intense vibrations than soft sounds

sound quality (timbre) —also sensed by cochlea so middle C played by a trumpet sounds different to that of a flute—different shaped sound waves (with harmonics) generated

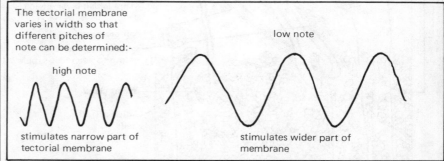

The tectorial membrane varies in width so that different pitches of note can be determined:-

low note

high note

stimulates narrow part of tectorial membrane

stimulates wider part of membrane

How direction of sound is determined

1. sound more intense in the ear nearest the source of sound
2. if the pitch is below 1500 cycles/second (third F above middle C), sound wave will bend around head and reach other ear before next sound wave so giving a different time of arrival in the ears.
   Using the above two features, either
   - *(i)* head kept still and person can point to sound source
   - or *(ii)* head moved till source is dead ahead (more accurate)
3. eyes used to determine precise origin of sound

Deafness

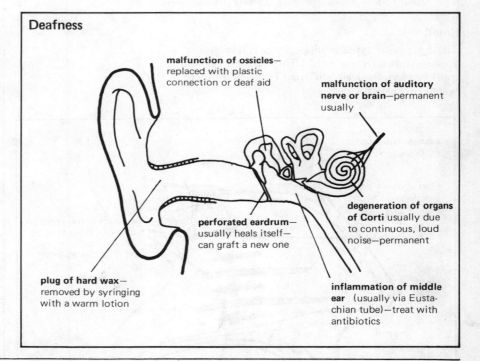

malfunction of ossicles—replaced with plastic connection or deaf aid

malfunction of auditory nerve or brain—permanent usually

perforated eardrum—usually heals itself—can graft a new one

degeneration of organs of Corti usually due to continuous, loud noise—permanent

plug of hard wax—removed by syringing with a warm lotion

inflammation of middle ear (usually via Eustachian tube)—treat with antibiotics

Touch

There are special nerve endings mostly just below the Malpighian layer. These are close together at fingertips, lips etc. but wide apart on soles of feet, arms, etc.

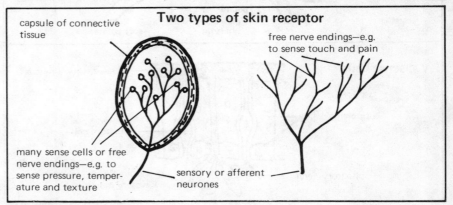

Two types of skin receptor

capsule of connective tissue

free nerve endings—e.g. to sense touch and pain

many sense cells or free nerve endings—e.g. to sense pressure, temperature and texture

sensory or afferent neurones

Touch, taste and smell

Probable positions of skin receptors

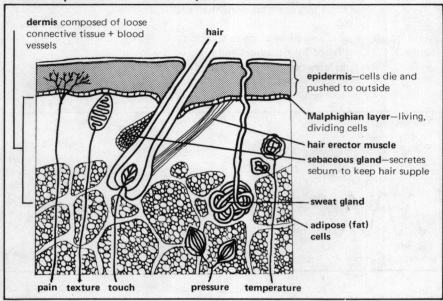

dermis composed of loose connective tissue + blood vessels

hair

epidermis—cells die and pushed to outside

Malphighian layer—living, dividing cells

hair erector muscle

sebaceous gland—secretes sebum to keep hair supple

sweat gland

adipose (fat) cells

pain texture touch pressure temperature

Smell

There are many types of olfactory cells responsible for detecting different smells. They all look alike but must be physiologically different (work in different ways).

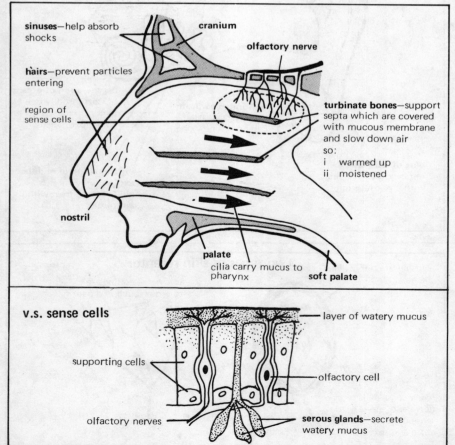

sinuses—help absorb shocks

cranium

olfactory nerve

hairs—prevent particles entering

region of sense cells

turbinate bones—support septa which are covered with mucous membrane and slow down air so:
i   warmed up
ii moistened

nostril

palate
cilia carry mucus to pharynx

soft palate

v.s. sense cells

layer of watery mucus

supporting cells

olfactory cell

olfactory nerves

serous glands—secrete watery mucus

Taste and smell

Both these senses detect chemical stimuli—the substance sensed must first dissolve before it stimulates sense cells. Little is known of how they work.

V.S. surface of tongue

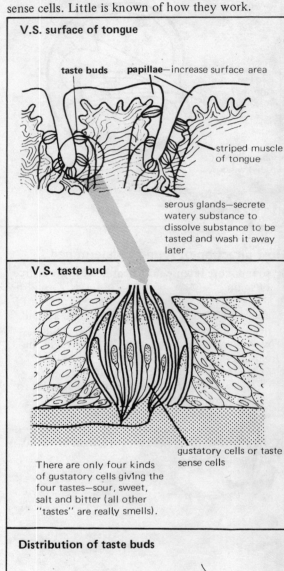

taste buds **papillae**—increase surface area

striped muscle of tongue

serous glands—secrete watery substance to dissolve substance to be tasted and wash it away later

V.S. taste bud

gustatory cells or taste sense cells

There are only four kinds of gustatory cells giving the four tastes—sour, sweet, salt and bitter (all other "tastes" are really smells).

Distribution of taste buds

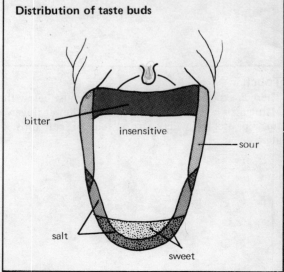

bitter

insensitive

sour

salt

sweet

Reproduction

The male and female reproductive systems

The male reproductive system

Sperms produced in each testis are stored temporarily in the epididymus. They then pass along the vas deferens. Swimming in a fluid called seminal fluid, produced by the seminal vesicles, prostate and Cowpers gland, they travel to the penis.

The male reproductive system as seen from the front

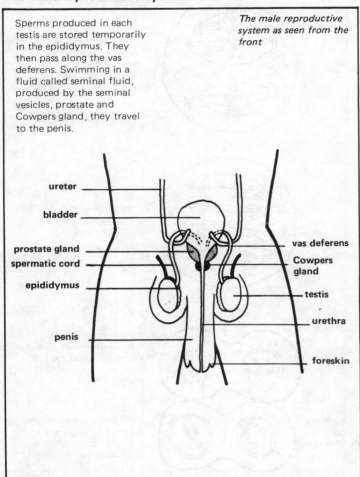

ureter
bladder
prostate gland
spermatic cord
epididymus
penis
vas deferens
Cowpers gland
testis
urethra
foreskin

This diagram shows the male reproductive system from the side

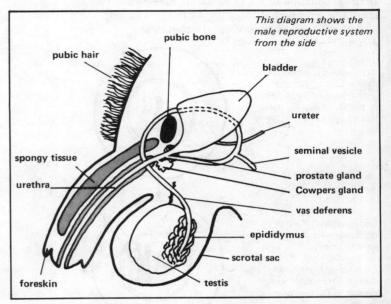

pubic hair
pubic bone
bladder
ureter
seminal vesicle
prostate gland
Cowpers gland
vas deferens
epididymus
scrotal sac
testis
spongy tissue
urethra
foreskin

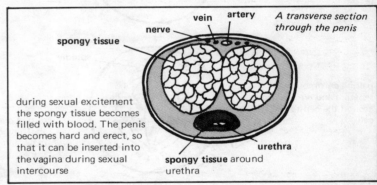

vein artery
nerve
spongy tissue
A transverse section through the penis

spongy tissue around urethra
urethra

during sexual excitement the spongy tissue becomes filled with blood. The penis becomes hard and erect, so that it can be inserted into the vagina during sexual intercourse

The female reproductive system

The diagram shows the female reproductive system as seen from the side

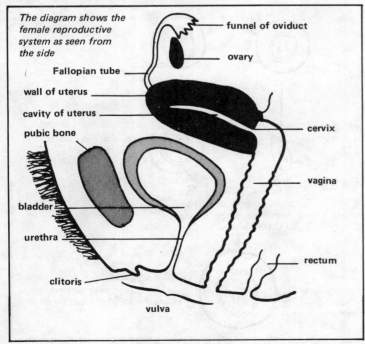

funnel of oviduct
ovary
Fallopian tube
wall of uterus
cavity of uterus
pubic bone
cervix
vagina
bladder
urethra
rectum
clitoris
vulva

The female reproductive system from the front

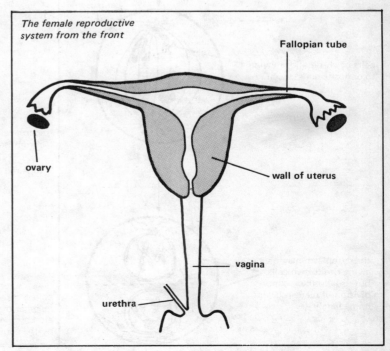

Fallopian tube
ovary
wall of uterus
vagina
urethra

Meiosis

In the production of the gametes, i.e. the ova and the sperms, a cell which is going to give rise to a gamete undergoes a special type of cell division called *Meiosis*.

1
a cell about to undergo meiosis. Note that the chromosomes are in pairs. In human beings each cell has 23 pairs of chromosomes

2
each member of a pair of chromosomes divides longitudinally

chromatids become entwined. An actual exchange of parts may take place

chromatids

3
pairing chromosomes separate and are arranged around the centre of the cell

spindle

4
pairs of chromatids moving to opposite ends of cell

centrosome

5
the cytoplasm may divide giving rise to two cells but usually the second division of meiosis begins immediately

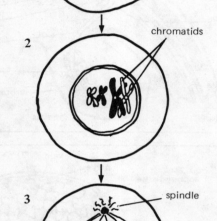

spindle

6
pairs of chromatids arranged around centre of cell attached to spindle by centromere spindles

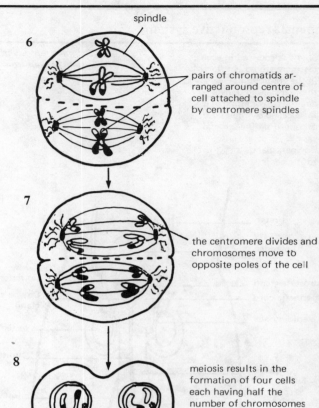

7
the centromere divides and chromosomes move to opposite poles of the cell

8
meiosis results in the formation of four cells each having half the number of chromosomes of the original dividing cell

these cells have only two chromosomes compared with four in the original dividing cell

during meiosis there is a shuffling of the genetic material on the chromosomes

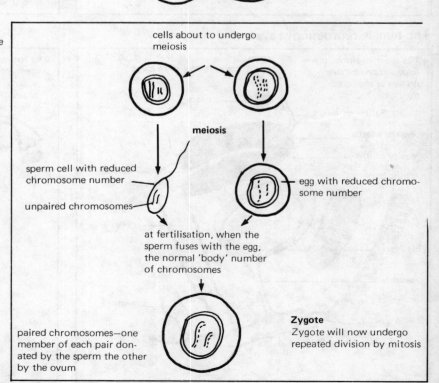

cells about to undergo meiosis

meiosis

sperm cell with reduced chromosome number

unpaired chromosomes

egg with reduced chromosome number

at fertilisation, when the sperm fuses with the egg, the normal 'body' number of chromosomes

paired chromosomes—one member of each pair donated by the sperm the other by the ovum

Zygote
Zygote will now undergo repeated division by mitosis

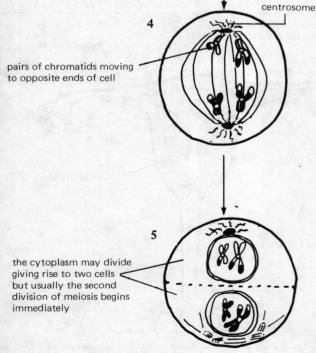

Fertilisation

The gonads i.e. the testes and ovaries are concerned with the production of the sex cells or gametes, the male spermatozoa and the female ova.

Ova—all the ova that will be produced are present in the ovary of a girl at birth. They do not however start to develop until puberty (10-13 years)

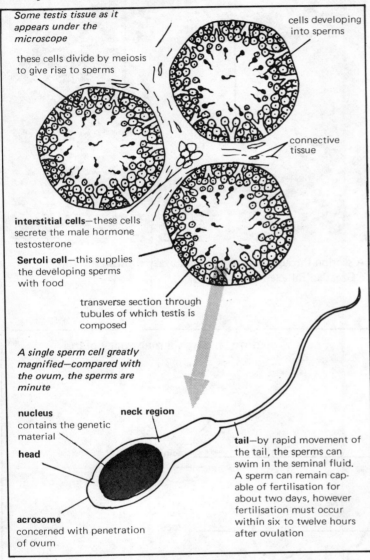

Some testis tissue as it appears under the microscope

cells developing into sperms

these cells divide by meiosis to give rise to sperms

connective tissue

interstitial cells—these cells secrete the male hormone testosterone

Sertoli cell—this supplies the developing sperms with food

transverse section through tubules of which testis is composed

A single sperm cell greatly magnified—compared with the ovum, the sperms are minute

nucleus
contains the genetic material

neck region

head

tail—by rapid movement of the tail, the sperms can swim in the seminal fluid. A sperm can remain capable of fertilisation for about two days, however fertilisation must occur within six to twelve hours after ovulation

acrosome
concerned with penetration of ovum

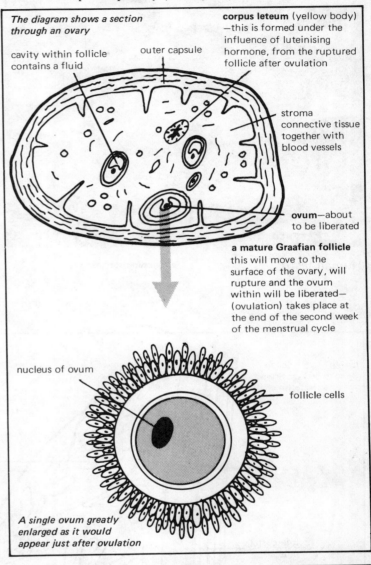

The diagram shows a section through an ovary

corpus leteum (yellow body) —this is formed under the influence of luteinising hormone, from the ruptured follicle after ovulation

cavity within follicle contains a fluid

outer capsule

stroma connective tissue together with blood vessels

ovum—about to be liberated

a mature Graafian follicle
this will move to the surface of the ovary, will rupture and the ovum within will be liberated— (ovulation) takes place at the end of the second week of the menstrual cycle

nucleus of ovum

follicle cells

A single ovum greatly enlarged as it would appear just after ovulation

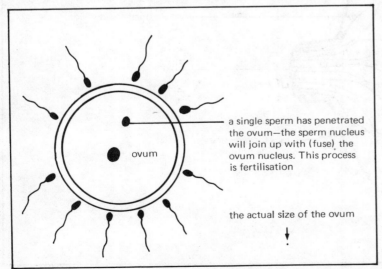

a single sperm has penetrated the ovum—the sperm nucleus will join up with (fuse) the ovum nucleus. This process is fertilisation

ovum

the actual size of the ovum

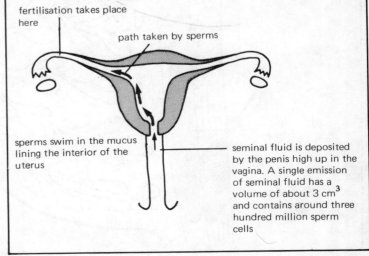

fertilisation takes place here

path taken by sperms

sperms swim in the mucus lining the interior of the uterus

seminal fluid is deposited by the penis high up in the vagina. A single emission of seminal fluid has a volume of about 3 cm^3 and contains around three hundred million sperm cells

Reproductive tissues

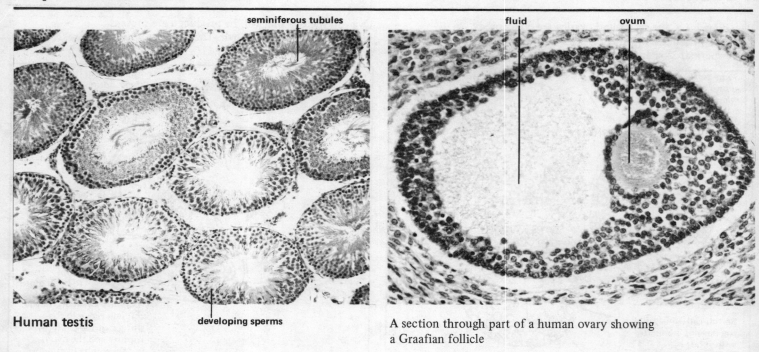

seminiferous tubules

fluid   ovum

Human testis   developing sperms

A section through part of a human ovary showing a Graafian follicle

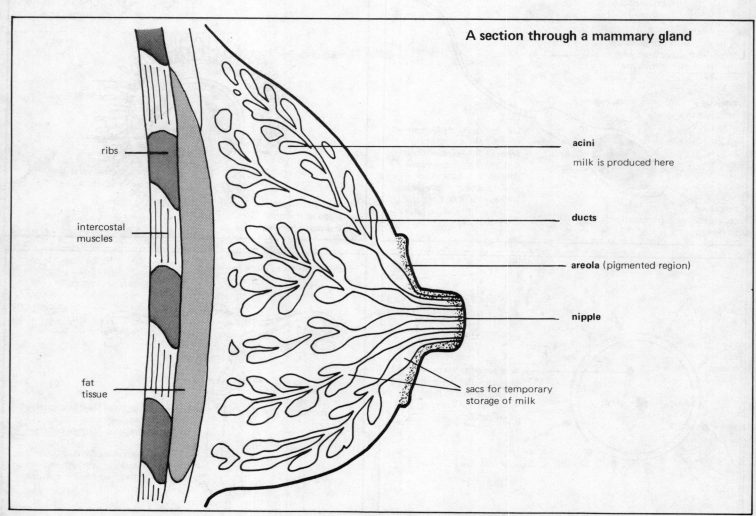

A section through a mammary gland

ribs

intercostal muscles

fat tissue

acini

milk is produced here

ducts

areola (pigmented region)

nipple

sacs for temporary storage of milk

Pregnancy

1 the ovum is caused to pass along the fallopian tube by the movement of the cilia

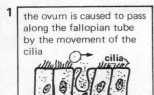

ciliated epithelium lining inner surface of fallopian tube

2 after the egg has been fertilised it undergoes mitosis

membrane of ovum

3 repeated mitotic division results in the formation of a ball of cells called a blastula

the blastula travels along the fallopian tube towards the uterus

fertilisation occurs here

an ovum released from the ovary passes into the funnel of the oviduct

the blastocyst burrows into the lining of the uterus that has been built up ready to receive it under the influence of the hormone oestrogen

4 these cells will give rise to the future embryo

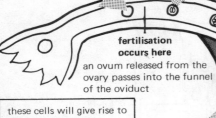

fluid-filled cavity

after many further mitotic divisions a hollow ball of cells known as a blastocyst is formed

5

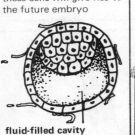

implantation

outgrowths from the blastocyst called trophoblastic villi, obtain food from the uterus wall

6 the blastocyst becomes entirely implanted about twelve days after fertilisation

trophoblastic villi obtaining food substances for developing embryo

wall of uterus

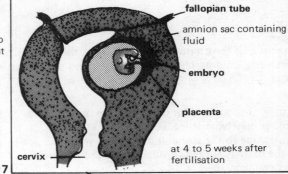

fallopian tube

amnion sac containing fluid

embryo

placenta

cervix

7 at 4 to 5 weeks after fertilisation

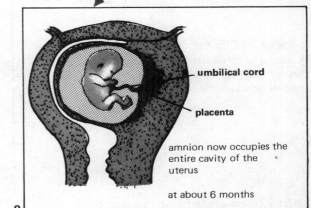

umbilical cord

placenta

amnion now occupies the entire cavity of the uterus

at about 6 months

8

food and oxygen pass from mothers' blood to babies' blood. Carbon dioxide and other waste substances pass from babies' blood to mother's blood to be excreted by mothers' excretory organs.
Note. Mothers' and babies' blood cells do not mix

mother's blood

baby's blood

foetal tissue   maternal tissue

artery

vein

umbilical cord

maternal blood vessels

space containing mother's blood

exchange of substances between mothers' and babies' blood occurs here

villus (projection buried in wall of uterus)

The placenta consists partly of foetal (developing baby) tissue and partly of maternal tissue. It is concerned with obtaining food and oxygen from mother's blood and with excretion

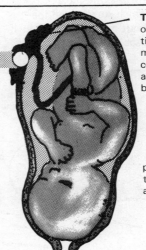

position of baby just prior to birth (around 9 months after fertilisation)

9

Birth

This usually takes place about 40 weeks after fertilisation of the egg.

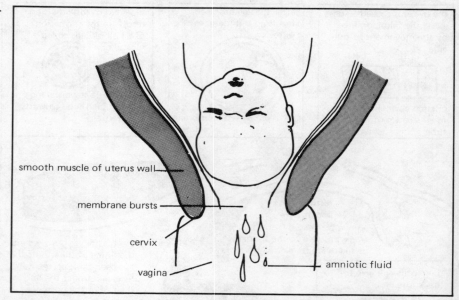

The neck of the uterus widens gradually, the amnion bursts and fluid passes along the vagina and out of the vulva.

During the contractions of the uterine muscles, the mother may experience labour pains. These are mostly due to the stretching of the cervix as the head of the baby is pushed/through it and pressure on the nerve endings there.

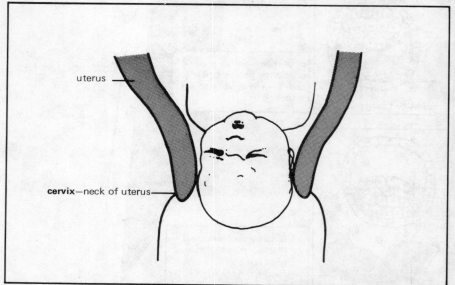

As the neck of the uterus widens, the baby is pushed by means of involuntary contractions of the uterine muscles and voluntary contraction of the abdominal muscles, through the neck of uterus.

About 15 minutes after birth, the placenta together with the remains of the umbilical cord and the membranes which surrounded the developing baby, is forced out of the body through the vagina by means of muscular contraction. It is known as the afterbirth.

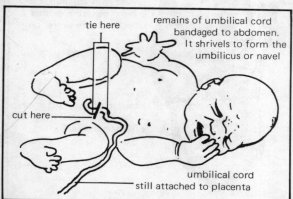

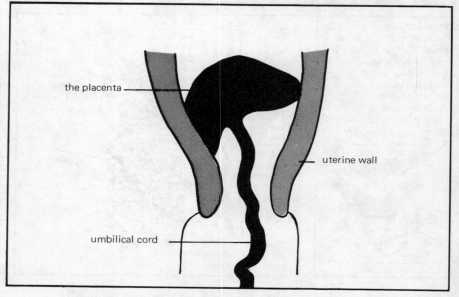

Contraception

The methods employed to prevent the birth of unwanted children. All methods of contraception either

1 Prevent sperm from coming into contact with and fertilising an ovum.
2 Preventing a fertilised ovum from implanting in the lining of the uterus.

(2) A technique preventing implantation

A small plastic structure is inserted by a doctor into the uterus.

The intra-uterine device or I.U.D.

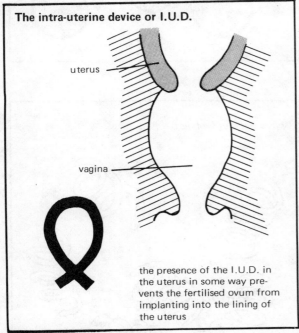

uterus

vagina

the presence of the I.U.D. in the uterus in some way prevents the fertilised ovum from implanting into the lining of the uterus

(3) Surgical techniques

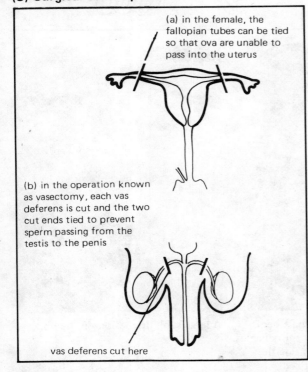

(a) in the female, the fallopian tubes can be tied so that ova are unable to pass into the uterus

(b) in the operation known as vasectomy, each vas deferens is cut and the two cut ends tied to prevent sperm passing from the testis to the penis

vas deferens cut here

(1) Techniques which prevent sperm and egg from meeting include:

(a) The sheath

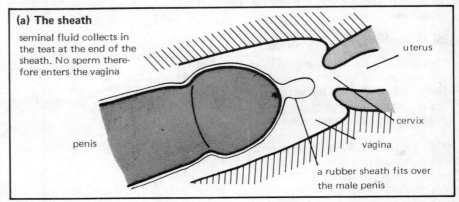

seminal fluid collects in the teat at the end of the sheath. No sperm therefore enters the vagina

uterus

cervix

vagina

penis

a rubber sheath fits over the male penis

(b) The cap or diaphragm

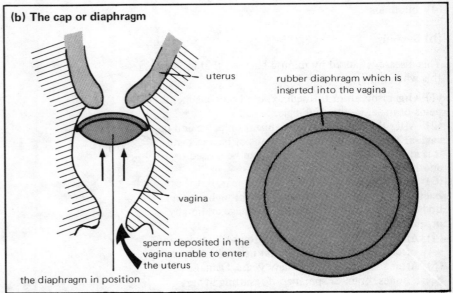

uterus

rubber diaphragm which is inserted into the vagina

vagina

sperm deposited in the vagina unable to enter the uterus

the diaphragm in position

(c) Oral contraceptives i.e. the contraceptive pill
(contains oestrogen and progesterone)

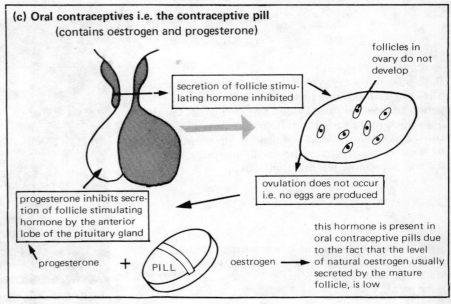

follicles in ovary do not develop

secretion of follicle stimulating hormone inhibited

ovulation does not occur i.e. no eggs are produced

progesterone inhibits secretion of follicle stimulating hormone by the anterior lobe of the pituitary gland

this hormone is present in oral contraceptive pills due to the fact that the level of natural oestrogen usually secreted by the mature follicle, is low

progesterone + PILL oestrogen

(d) Spermicidal chemicals
Chemical substances which are placed in the vagina before intercourse takes place. They kill sperms before they can enter the uterus.

Venereal diseases

These are diseases which are spread from one person to another during sexual intercourse. There are two main venereal diseases.

(a) Gonorrhoea

This disease is caused by bacteria that look like this when viewed under the microscope. They enter the body through mucous membranes, usually the membrane covering the end of the penis or the membrane lining the interior of the vagina.

They cause the following symptoms:
(1) Inflammation of the vaginal lining in the female, or urethra in the male.
(2) sterility
(3) inflammation of joints
(4) blindness

(b) Syphilis

This disease is caused by minute bacteria that look like this when highly magnified

(1) Organisms enter through exposed mucous membrane, penis of male, vagina of female.
(2) After three weeks. Ulcers appear on penis and in vagina. These contain many millions of bacteria and it is at this stage when the disease can be passed on to another person.
(3) After six weeks. The ulcers disappear, but the bacteria enter the blood and spread throughout the body. A rash usually appears at this stage and many organs become inflamed and painful.
(4) After twelve weeks. The symptoms disappear and very often the person believes that he or she is cured.
(5) After some time often many years. Damage to heart, bones, brain or spinal cord resulting in very serious illness, insanity, paralysis and finally death.

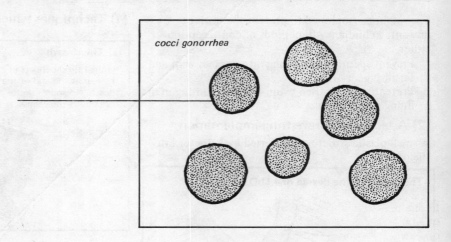
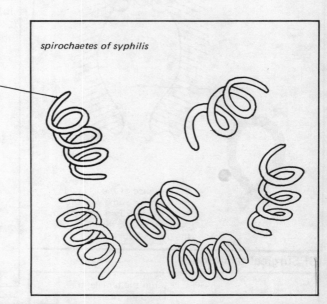

cocci gonorrhea

spirochaetes of syphilis

Photographs supplied by the Wellcome Museum of Medical Science

Both gonorrhoea and syphilis are very serious diseases. They can lead to very serious illness in the affected person and may be passed on by a mother to her unborn child. In the early stages both diseases may be cured by antibiotics, usually penicillin. The wearing by the male of a contraceptive sheath may reduce but will not remove the risk of infection.

Note: there are other sexually transmitted diseases including one caused by Herpes (a virus) which cannot be cured by antibiotics.

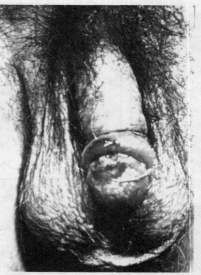
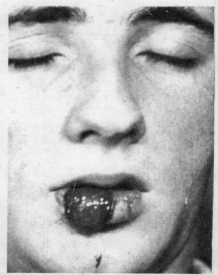

A syphilitic lesion on the male penis, containing millions of tiny spirochaetes. In women the lesions are inside the vagina and may not be noticed.

A large syphilitic lesion on the lip.

Genetics
The principles

Gregor Mendel, an abbot who lived in Czechoslovakia during the nineteenth century, used pea plants in many breeding experiments and discovered the basic principles of genetics, the science which deals with the way in which characteristics are passed from generation to generation.

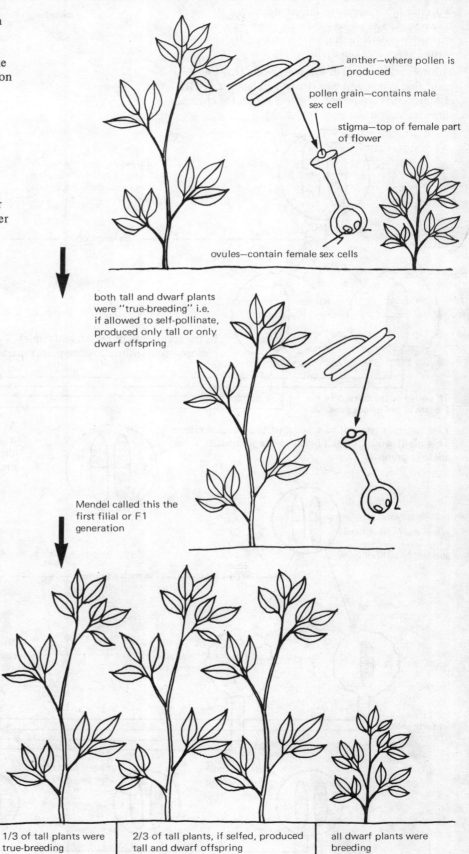

anther—where pollen is produced

pollen grain—contains male sex cell

stigma—top of female part of flower

In one of Mendel's experiments, pollen from a flower of a tall pea plant was placed on the stigma of a flower of a dwarf pea plant.

ovules—contain female sex cells

both tall and dwarf plants were "true-breeding" i.e. if allowed to self-pollinate, produced only tall or only dwarf offspring

The seeds were collected, planted and allowed to germinate. All developed into tall plants, there were no dwarf plants.

Mendel then self-pollinated the plants of the F1 generation i.e. he transferred pollen from the anther to the stigma of the same flower.

Mendel called this the first filial or F1 generation

The seeds were collected, planted and allowed to germinate. Mendel found that about ¾ of the seedlings developed into tall plants, only about ¼ were dwarf and there were no plants of intermediate height.

Mendel called this the second filial or F2 generation

1/3 of tall plants were true-breeding

2/3 of tall plants, if selfed, produced tall and dwarf offspring

all dwarf plants were breeding

Principles explained

With our more advanced knowledge about the structure of cells and of how they divide, we are able to explain Mendel's findings in terms of cells, chromosomes, genes and cell division.

This represents a cell in the anther of a true-breeding plant that is going to give rise to a pollen grain. The chromosomes are paired. The line across the chromosome represents the gene for height.

This represents a cell in the ovule of a dwarf pea plant that is going to develop into an ovule or egg.

the height gene has two forms or alleles. One allele T is responsible for tallness, the other t for dwarfness

meiosis occurs

pollen

ovules

In the formation of pollen and ovules meiosis occurs; chromosome pairs separate.

All ovules carry the t allele of the height gene

All pollen grains carry only the T allele of the height gene

This represents a cell of a plant of the F1 generation. This plant would be tall because the dominant T allele is present.

At fertilisation when male and female gametes join together, a cell is produced which has both T and t alleles of the height gene. The T is dominant so that such cells will develop into tall plants.

when the plants of the F1 generation were allowed to self-pollinate

meiosis occurs

pollen

ovules

50% of the pollen grains and ovules carry the T and 50% the t allele

two types of pollen produced

two types of ovule produced

at fertilisation

this would be true-breeding

these would not be true-breeding

this would be true-breeding

all these will become tall plants

this will become a dwarf plant

The inheritance of eye colour in man

The laws governing the inheritance of characteristics as put forward by Gregor Mendel can be applied to the inheritance of eye colour in man.

In this diagram a man with brown eyes is married to a woman with blue eyes.

Brown eyed man
both alleles of the eye colour gene are dominant

B   B

X

Blue eyed woman
both alleles of the eye colour gene are recessive

b   b

at meiosis pairs of chromosomes separate

sperm

B

b   ovum

dominant allele of eye colour gene present

B   b

all their children will have brown eyes

some people with brown eyes are **heterozygous** (with dominant and recessive alleles present) i.e. two alleles of eye colour gene are present

B   b

Brown eyed man   X   Blue eyed woman

b   b

must be **homozygous** (only one kind of allele of eye colour present)

sperms

B   b

at meiosis

b   b   ova

at fertilisation

B   b

brown eyes

B   b

brown eyes

b   b

blue eyes

b   b

blue eyes

2 brown eyed children

2 blue eyed children

the probability of any child of this couple of having blue eyes would be 50%

Dihybrid inheritance

An example of inheritance involving two characteristics—i.e. dihybrid inheritance

If a brown eyed, brown haired man marries a woman with blue eyes and red hair, what would be the possible eye and hair colour of the children? The genes for hair colour and eye colour are on different pairs of chromosomes.

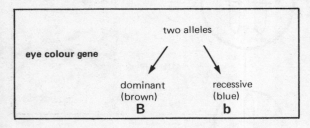

eye colour gene — two alleles — dominant (brown) **B** / recessive (blue) **b**

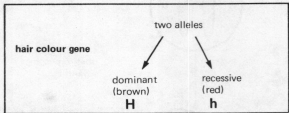

hair colour gene — two alleles — dominant (brown) **H** / recessive (red) **h**

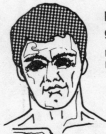

Possible genotypes

brown eyed, brown haired man

Possible genotype

blue eyed, red haired woman

a. BBHH   **b.** BbHH   **c.** BBHh   **d.** BbHh

bbhh

if man has genotype a:

	bh (eggs)	eyes	hair	
BH (sperm)	BbHh	brown	brown	all children

if man has genotype d:

	bh	eyes	hair	
BH	BbHh	brown	brown	25%
Bh	Bbhh	brown	red	25%
bH	bbHh	blue	brown	25%
bh	bbhh	blue	red	25%

if man has genotype b:

	bh	eyes	hair	
BH	BbHh	brown	brown	50%
bH	bbHh	blue	brown	50%

if man has genotype c:

	bh	eyes	hair	
BH	BbHh	brown	brown	50%
Bh	Bbhh	brown	red	50%

Blood groups

There are four main blood groups: A, B AB and O

A person's blood group depends upon minute structures on the outside of the red blood cells known as agglutinogens. There are two agglutinogens A and B

There are substances in the plasma called agglutinins, anti A and anti B

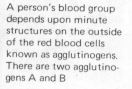

agglutinogen

plasma

red blood cells

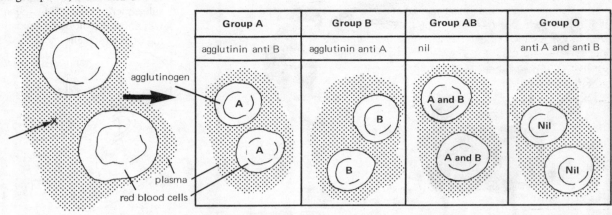

Group A	Group B	Group AB	Group O
agglutinin anti B	agglutinin anti A	nil	anti A and anti B

person with group B blood being given a blood transfusion with group A blood

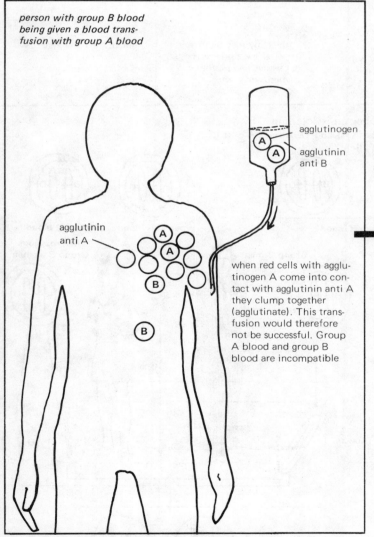

agglutinogen

agglutinin anti B

agglutinin anti A

when red cells with agglutinogen A come into contact with agglutinin anti A they clump together (agglutinate). This transfusion would therefore not be successful. Group A blood and group B blood are incompatible

All persons may be given blood group O in transfusions.

Persons having group O blood are therefore universal donors.

Persons who have group AB blood, can be given blood of any group and are therefore universal recipients.

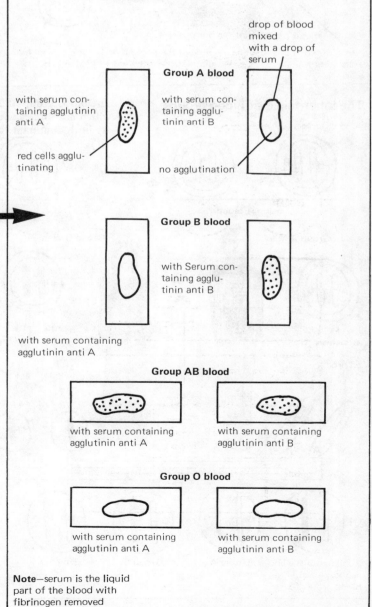

The slide agglutination test

drop of blood mixed with a drop of serum

Group A blood

with serum containing agglutinin anti A

with serum containing agglutinin anti B

red cells agglutinating

no agglutination

Group B blood

with Serum containing agglutinin anti B

with serum containing agglutinin anti A

Group AB blood

with serum containing agglutinin anti A

with serum containing agglutinin anti B

Group O blood

with serum containing agglutinin anti A

with serum containing agglutinin anti B

Note—serum is the liquid part of the blood with fibrinogen removed

The rhesus (Rh) factor

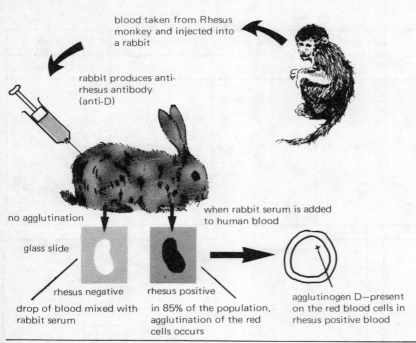

blood taken from Rhesus monkey and injected into a rabbit

rabbit produces anti-rhesus antibody (anti-D)

no agglutination

glass slide

rhesus negative

drop of blood mixed with rabbit serum

when rabbit serum is added to human blood

rhesus positive

in 85% of the population, agglutination of the red cells occurs

agglutinogen D—present on the red blood cells in rhesus positive blood

In the later stages of pregnancy or especially in subsequent pregnancies, the anti-rhesus antibody will enter the blood of the baby and cause clumping of the red cells

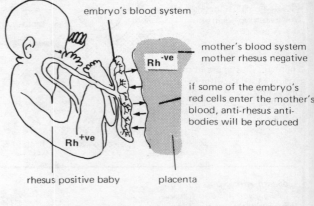

embryo's blood system

mother's blood system
mother rhesus negative

Rh^{-ve}

if some of the embryo's red cells enter the mother's blood, anti-rhesus antibodies will be produced

Rh^{+ve}

rhesus positive baby

placenta

the baby may be rhesus positive if father is rhesus positive and mother is rhesus negative

at birth the baby may have all of its rhesus +ve blood replaced by rhesus negative blood

The inheritance of blood groups

The blood group of a person is determined by a gene which has three alleles, A, B and O. Alleles A and B are both dominant to allele O.

blood group genotypes

group A blood

group B blood

group A B blood

group O blood

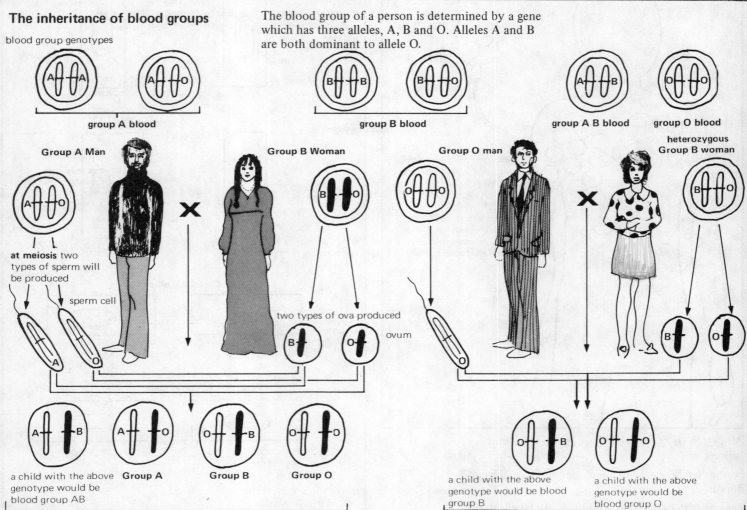

Group A Man

Group B Woman

Group O man

heterozygous
Group B woman

at meiosis two types of sperm will be produced

sperm cell

two types of ova produced

ovum

a child with the above genotype would be blood group AB

Group A

Group B

Group O

a child with the above genotype would be blood group B

a child with the above genotype would be blood group O

possible blood groups of children

any child born to the above couple would be either group B or O

Inherited diseases

Diseases which can be transmitted from one generation to another are known as hereditary diseases

The condition known as hare-lip is due to the possession of a recessive allele which we shall call (h). In most people only the dominant allele of the gene (H) is present. They would therefore have the genotype HH

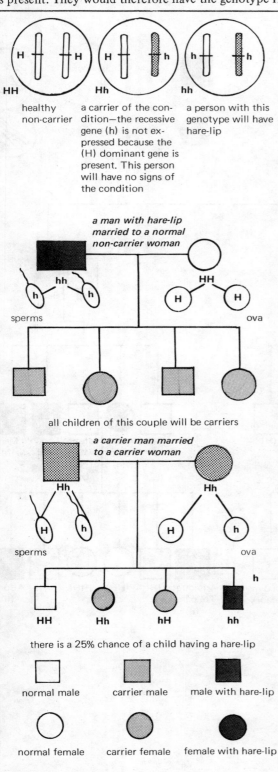

HH
healthy non-carrier

Hh
a carrier of the condition—the recessive gene (h) is not expressed because the (H) dominant gene is present. This person will have no signs of the condition

hh
a person with this genotype will have hare-lip

a man with hare-lip married to a normal non-carrier woman

hh sperms

HH ova

all children of this couple will be carriers

a carrier man married to a carrier woman

Hh sperms

Hh ova

h

HH   Hh   hH   hh

there is a 25% chance of a child having a hare-lip

normal male   carrier male   male with hare-lip

normal female   carrier female   female with hare-lip

The inheritance of sex

In the nucleus of each cell of the body there are 22 pairs of chromosomes plus 2 sex chromosomes. One is known as the X chromosome the other as the Y chromosome. All males have an X and a Y chromosome. All females have 2 X chromosomes

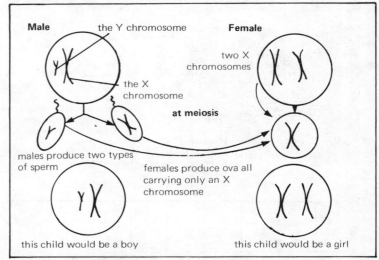

Male   the Y chromosome   **Female**

two X chromosomes

the X chromosome

at meiosis

males produce two types of sperm

females produce ova all carrying only an X chromosome

this child would be a boy   this child would be a girl

The inheritance of haemophilia

Haemophilia is a hereditary disease in which the blood **does not clot** so that even a very minor injury can lead to serious haemorrhage (bleeding)

Gene H has two alleles (H) is dominant, when present the person does not have haemophilia. (h) is recessive, when two (h) alleles are present, the person will have the condition.

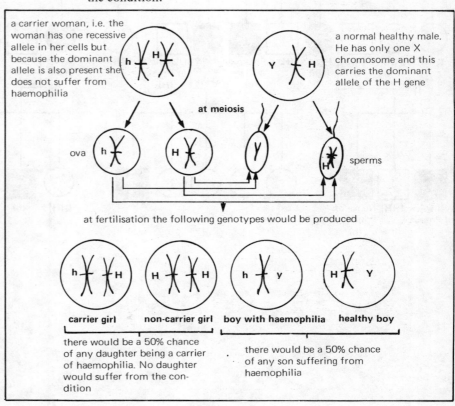

a carrier woman, i.e. the woman has one recessive allele in her cells but because the dominant allele is also present she does not suffer from haemophilia

a normal healthy male. He has only one X chromosome and this carries the dominant allele of the H gene

at meiosis

ova   sperms

at fertilisation the following genotypes would be produced

carrier girl   **non-carrier girl**   **boy with haemophilia**   **healthy boy**

there would be a 50% chance of any daughter being a carrier of haemophilia. No daughter would suffer from the condition

there would be a 50% chance of any son suffering from haemophilia

Haemophilia

**The family tree of Queen Victoria showing how
the disease haemophilia is inherited**

the gene causing haemophilia
is on the X chromosome.
The gene (called gene H here)
has two alleles, dominant H,
recessive h.

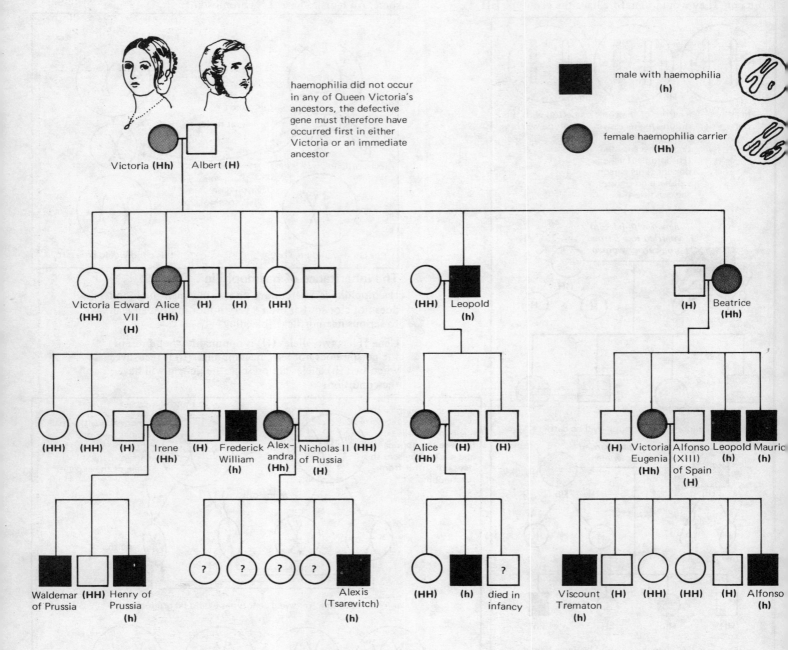

haemophilia did not occur
in any of Queen Victoria's
ancestors, the defective
gene must therefore have
occurred first in either
Victoria or an immediate
ancestor

male with haemophilia
(h)

female haemophilia carrier
(Hh)

Victoria **(Hh)**   Albert **(H)**

Victoria **(HH)**   Edward VII **(H)**   Alice **(Hh)**   **(H)**   **(H)**   **(HH)**   **(HH)**   Leopold **(h)**   **(H)**   Beatrice **(Hh)**

(HH)   **(HH)**   **(H)**   Irene **(Hh)**   **(H)**   Frederick William **(h)**   Alexandra **(Hh)**   Nicholas II of Russia **(H)**   **(HH)**   Alice **(Hh)**   **(H)**   **(H)**   **(H)**   Victoria Eugenia **(Hh)**   Alfonso (XIII) of Spain **(H)**   Leopold **(h)**   Mauric **(h)**

Waldemar of Prussia   **(HH)** Henry of Prussia **(h)**   ?   ?   ?   ?   Alexis (Tsarevitch) **(h)**   **(HH)**   **(h)**   died in infancy ?   Viscount Trematon **(h)**   **(H)**   **(HH)**   **(HH)**   **(H)**   Alfonso **(h)**

How a gene works

the dark skin of a negro is due to the presence of a coloured chemical or pigment in the cells of the skin. A gene which we shall call gene P controls the production of this pigment

gene P occasionally changes (mutates) to form a recessive allele p. In the diagram husband and wife both carry dominant allele P and recessive allele p of the pigment gene

For the production of the skin pigment an enzyme is necessary. This enzyme is a protein and is assembled on a ribosome in the cytoplasm according to instructions on a chromosome in the nucleus. One gene is responsible for one protein. In the case of the albino negro the cells do not carry a gene for the production of the enzyme necessary for pigment production.

heterozygous parents

meiosis occurs in the production of ova, 50% of ova carry the P allele, 50% carry the allele p

Meiosis occurs in the production of sperms

50% of sperms carry the P allele, 50% carry the p allele

there is a 75% chance that any child of this couple will carry the P allele and will therefore have the pigment and dark skin

there is a 25% chance that a child will be homozygous for the recessive allele p. This child will not have pigment and his skin will be pale. He will be white

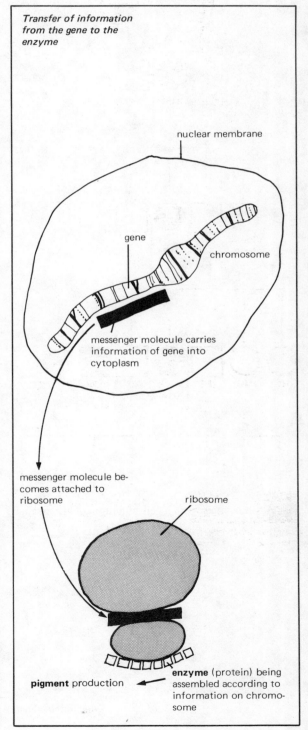

Transfer of information from the gene to the enzyme

nuclear membrane

gene

chromosome

messenger molecule carries information of gene into cytoplasm

messenger molecule becomes attached to ribosome

ribosome

pigment production ←

enzyme (protein) being assembled according to information on chromosome

Mongolism

Twin sisters: the girl on the right is a mongol.

The chromosomes from a cell of a mongol girl arranged in pairs.

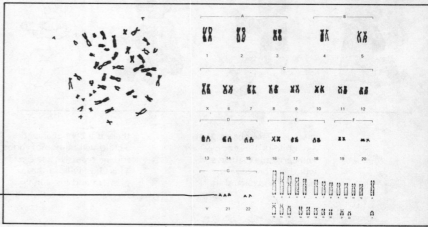

one extra chromosome is found in the mongol

Support and movement

The human skeleton

The skeleton gives the body a rigid framework. Muscles attached to bones contract and cause movements of parts of or all of the body.

Human skeleton

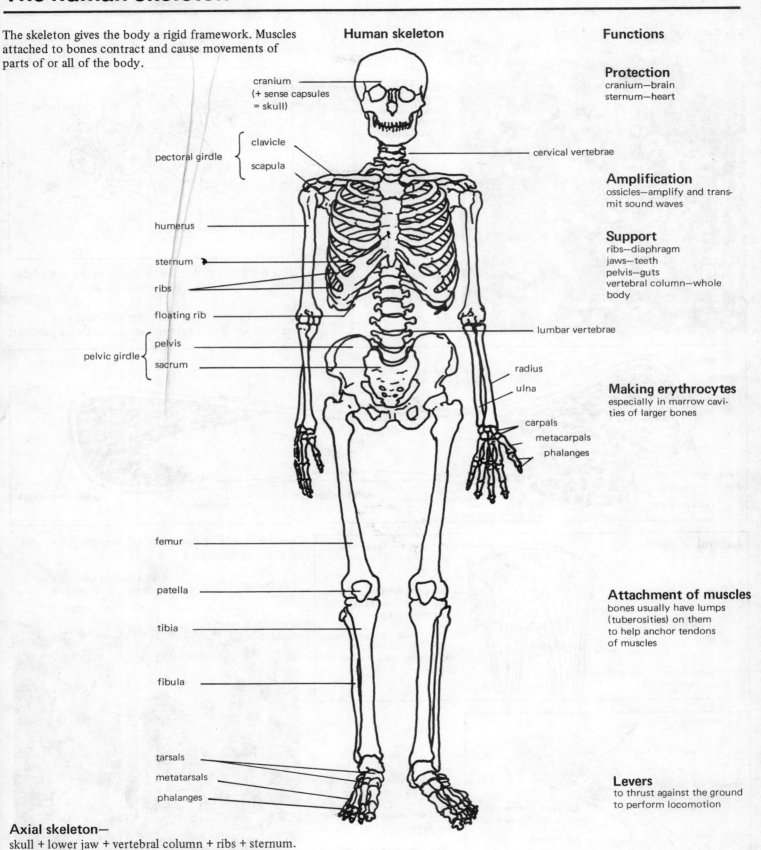

cranium
(+ sense capsules
= skull)

pectoral girdle { clavicle
scapula

humerus

sternum

ribs

floating rib

pelvic girdle { pelvis
sacrum

cervical vertebrae

lumbar vertebrae

radius

ulna

carpals

metacarpals

phalanges

femur

patella

tibia

fibula

tarsals

metatarsals

phalanges

Functions

Protection
cranium—brain
sternum—heart

Amplification
ossicles—amplify and transmit sound waves

Support
ribs—diaphragm
jaws—teeth
pelvis—guts
vertebral column—whole body

Making erythrocytes
especially in marrow cavities of larger bones

Attachment of muscles
bones usually have lumps (tuberosities) on them to help anchor tendons of muscles

Levers
to thrust against the ground to perform locomotion

Axial skeleton—
skull + lower jaw + vertebral column + ribs + sternum.

Appendicular skeleton—
bones of limbs + pectoral girdle + pelvic girdle.

Cartilages and tendons

t.s. cartilage

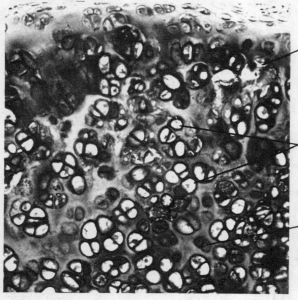

food, oxygen etc. diffuse from blood vessels in perichondrium (membrane around outside) to chondroblasts

chondroblasts—living cells in cartilage

chondrin—the matrix secreted by chondroblasts

If flexible cartilage is needed, yellow, elastic fibres are enclosed in the chondrin matrix:

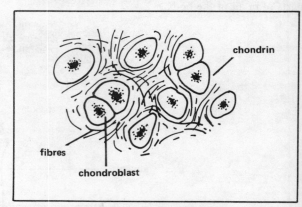

chondrin

fibres

chondroblast

This is elastic cartilage and is found in the end of the nose, the epiglottis, the external ear etc.

See also fibrocartilage (cartilage with white, collagenous fibres) between vertebrae, in the pelvis etc.

l.s. whole bone

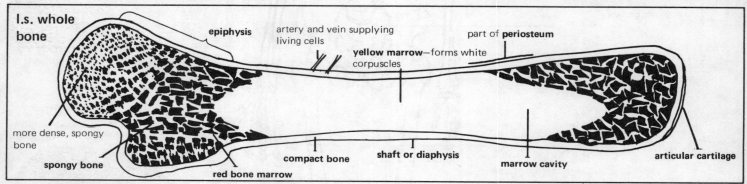

epiphysis

artery and vein supplying living cells

yellow marrow—forms white corpuscles

part of **periosteum**

more dense, spongy bone

spongy bone

red bone marrow

compact bone

shaft or diaphysis

marrow cavity

articular cartilage

l.s. end of bone

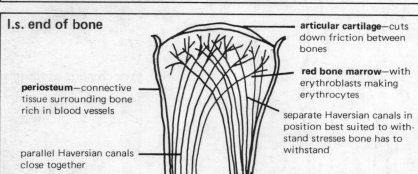

articular cartilage—cuts down friction between bones

red bone marrow—with erythroblasts making erythrocytes

periosteum—connective tissue surrounding bone rich in blood vessels

separate Haversian canals in position best suited to withstand stresses bone has to withstand

parallel Haversian canals close together

l.s. tendon

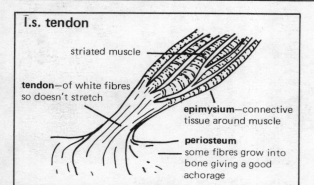

striated muscle

tendon—of white fibres so doesn't stretch

epimysium—connective tissue around muscle

periosteum some fibres grow into bone giving a good achorage

Bone is chiefly composed of calcium phosphate and calcium carbonate

t.s. bone

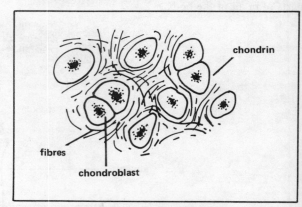

small, radiating canals taking food, oxygen etc. to osteocytes

Haversian canal—contains blood vessels

bone tissue—calcium salts + fibres

a Haversian system

osteocytes (living cells)

Ossification

There are two ways of forming bone:

1 Membrane bone—bone is formed in sheets of connective tissue. e.g. bones of cranium.

2 Cartilage bone—bone replaces cartilage of young person. This is the commonest method of ossification and allows the skeleton to grow:

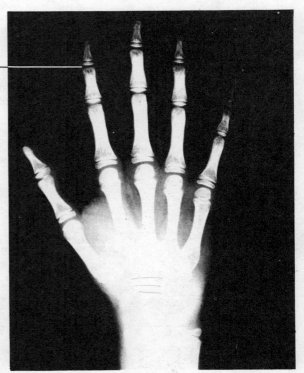

gap where no bone formed yet (cartilage doesn't show up well on radiograph)

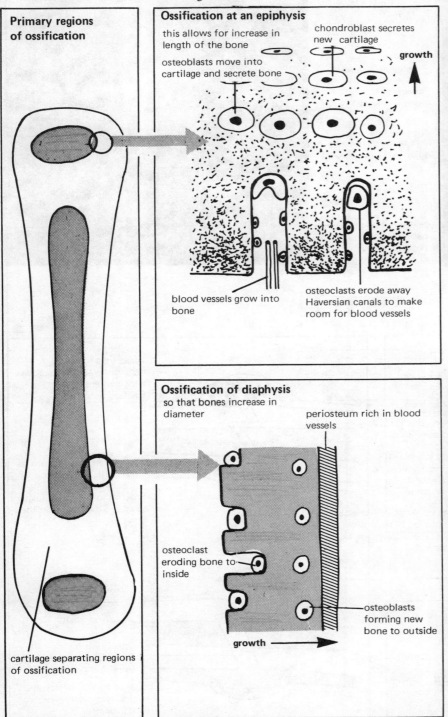

Primary regions of ossification

cartilage separating regions of ossification

Ossification at an epiphysis

this allows for increase in length of the bone

chondroblast secretes new cartilage

osteoblasts move into cartilage and secrete bone

growth

blood vessels grow into bone

osteoclasts erode away Haversian canals to make room for blood vessels

Ossification of diaphysis
so that bones increase in diameter

periosteum rich in blood vessels

osteoclast eroding bone to inside

osteoblasts forming new bone to outside

growth

Radiograph of child's hand

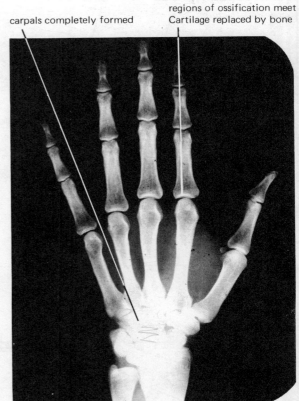

carpals completely formed

regions of ossification meet Cartilage replaced by bone

Radiograph of adult's hand

The rate at which bone is formed is controlled by a hormone secreted by the parathyroid gland. Vitamin D is also needed for the process of ossification.

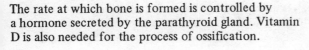

Fractures

Radiograph of facture of femur

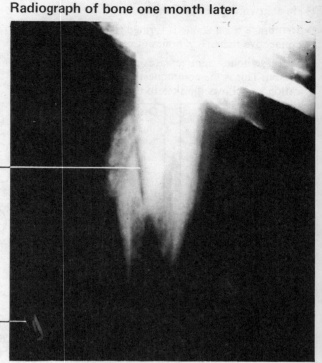

osteoblasts have secreted new bone to join broken ends

clot forms between broken bones (doesn't show up on radiograph)

Radiograph of bone one month later

safety pin tying bandages—X rays will not pass through metal

A. Simple fracture

The bones break but do not pierce skin (see example of healing)

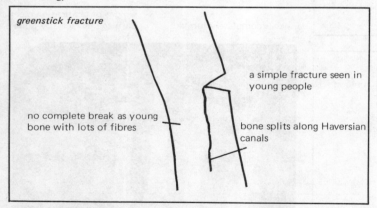

greenstick fracture

no complete break as young bone with lots of fibres

a simple fracture seen in young people

bone splits along Haversian canals

B. Compound fracture

The pieces of bone pierce the skin. These fractures are more serious and take longer to heal.

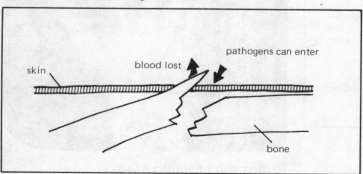

skin

blood lost

pathogens can enter

bone

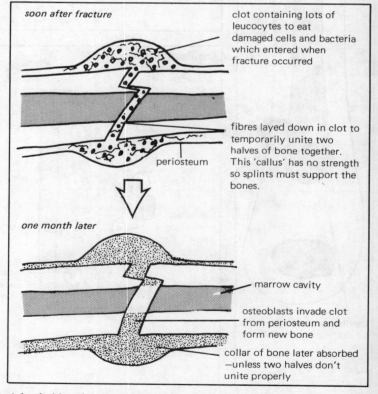

soon after fracture

clot containing lots of leucocytes to eat damaged cells and bacteria which entered when fracture occurred

fibres layed down in clot to temporarily unite two halves of bone together. This 'callus' has no strength so splints must support the bones.

periosteum

one month later

marrow cavity

osteoblasts invade clot from periosteum and form new bone

collar of bone later absorbed —unless two halves don't unite properly

A healed break is usually stronger than the unbroken bone so it is unlikely to fracture in the same place again.

Vertebrae

Generalised vertebra

Superior (front end) view

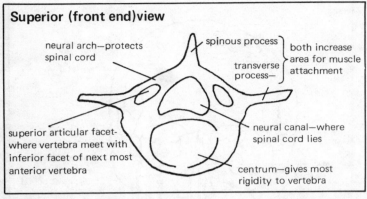

neural arch—protects spinal cord

spinous process

transverse process—

both increase area for muscle attachment

superior articular facet— where vertebra meet with inferior facet of next most anterior vertebra

neural canal—where spinal cord lies

centrum—gives most rigidity to vertebra

Lateral (side view)

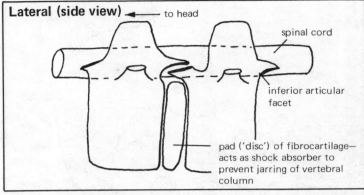

to head

spinal cord

inferior articular facet

pad ('disc') of fibrocartilage— acts as shock absorber to prevent jarring of vertebral column

Superior view of atlas (first cervical vertebra)

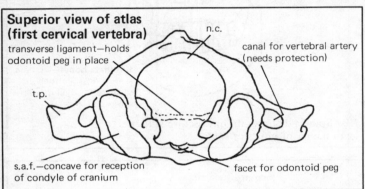

transverse ligament—holds odontoid peg in place

n.c.

canal for vertebral artery (needs protection)

t.p.

s.a.f.—concave for reception of condyle of cranium

facet for odontoid peg

Lateral view of axis (second cervical vertebra)

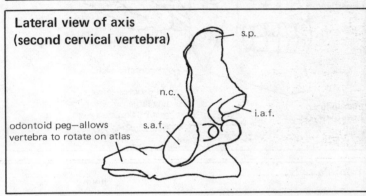

s.p.

n.c.

i.a.f.

s.a.f.

odontoid peg—allows vertebra to rotate on atlas

Numbers of vertebrae

Cervical 7
Thoracic 12
Lumbar 5
Sacral 5 (fused)
Coccygeal 4-5

Typical cervical vertebra

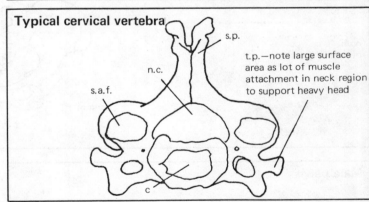

s.p.

n.c.

t.p.—note large surface area as lot of muscle attachment in neck region to support heavy head

s.a.f.

c

Thoracic vertebra

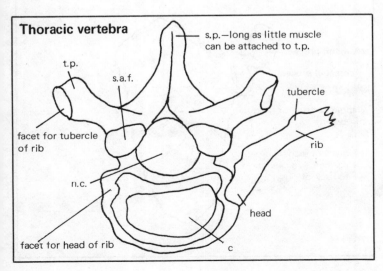

s.p.—long as little muscle can be attached to t.p.

t.p.

s.a.f.

tubercle

facet for tubercle of rib

rib

n.c.

head

facet for head of rib

c

Lumbar vertebra

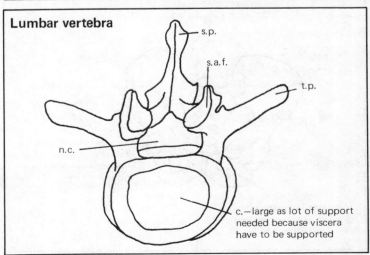

s.p.

s.a.f.

t.p.

n.c.

c.—large as lot of support needed because viscera have to be supported

Skull, pelvis and scapula

Skull—side view

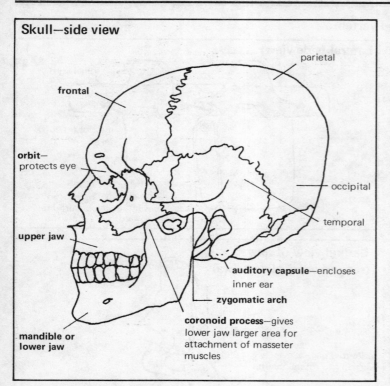

frontal

parietal

orbit—
protects eye

occipital

temporal

upper jaw

auditory capsule—encloses
inner ear

zygomatic arch

mandible or
lower jaw

coronoid process—gives
lower jaw larger area for
attachment of masseter
muscles

Skull—front view

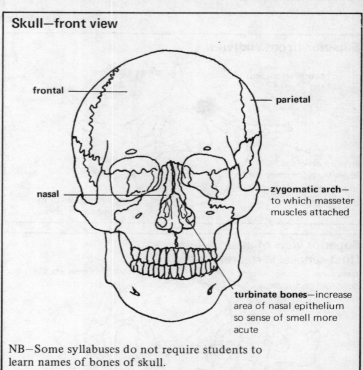

frontal

parietal

nasal

zygomatic arch—
to which masseter
muscles attached

turbinate bones—increase
area of nasal epithelium
so sense of smell more
acute

NB—Some syllabuses do not require students to
learn names of bones of skull.

Female pelvis

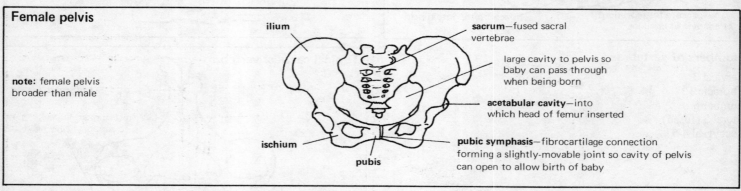

note: female pelvis
broader than male

ilium

sacrum—fused sacral
vertebrae

large cavity to pelvis so
baby can pass through
when being born

acetabular cavity—into
which head of femur inserted

ischium

pubis

pubic symphasis—fibrocartilage connection
forming a slightly-movable joint so cavity of pelvis
can open to allow birth of baby

Male pelvis

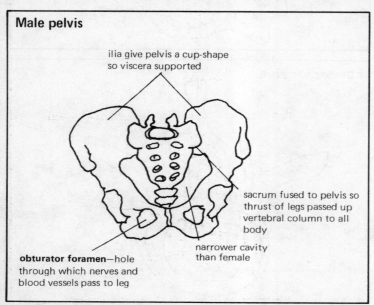

ilia give pelvis a cup-shape
so viscera supported

sacrum fused to pelvis so
thrust of legs passed up
vertebral column to all
body

narrower cavity
than female

obturator foramen—hole
through which nerves and
blood vessels pass to leg

Scapula

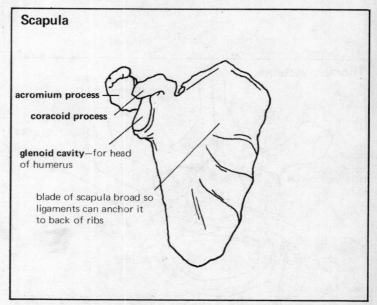

acromium process

coracoid process

glenoid cavity—for head
of humerus

blade of scapula broad so
ligaments can anchor it
to back of ribs

Limb skeleton

The basic plan for the skeleton of the arm is the same as that of the leg but different names are given to the bones:

Tuberosities—projections on bones where tendons of muscles attached.

Condyles—ends of bones which articulate with next.

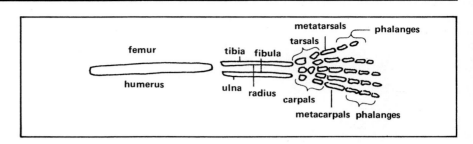

Arm

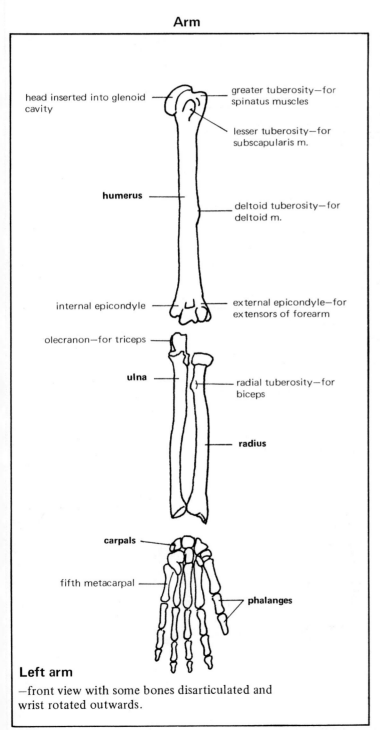

head inserted into glenoid cavity

greater tuberosity—for spinatus muscles

lesser tuberosity—for subscapularis m.

humerus

deltoid tuberosity—for deltoid m.

internal epicondyle

external epicondyle—for extensors of forearm

olecranon—for triceps

ulna

radial tuberosity—for biceps

radius

carpals

fifth metacarpal

phalanges

Left arm
—front view with some bones disarticulated and wrist rotated outwards.

Leg

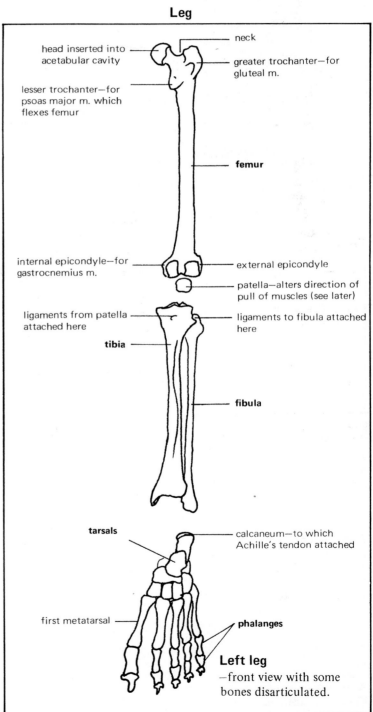

head inserted into acetabular cavity

neck

greater trochanter—for gluteal m.

lesser trochanter—for psoas major m. which flexes femur

femur

internal epicondyle—for gastrocnemius m.

external epicondyle

patella—alters direction of pull of muscles (see later)

ligaments from patella attached here

ligaments to fibula attached here

tibia

fibula

tarsals

calcaneum—to which Achille's tendon attached

first metatarsal

phalanges

Left leg
—front view with some bones disarticulated.

Muscles

A skeletal muscle

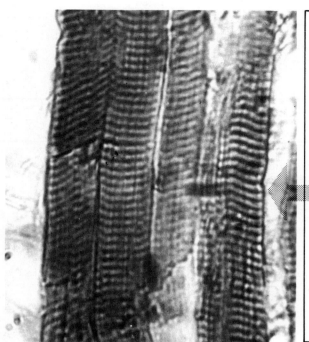

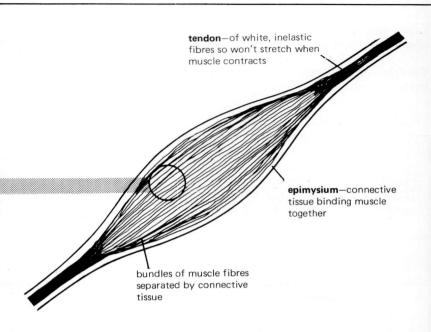

tendon—of white, inelastic fibres so won't stretch when muscle contracts

epimysium—connective tissue binding muscle together

bundles of muscle fibres separated by connective tissue

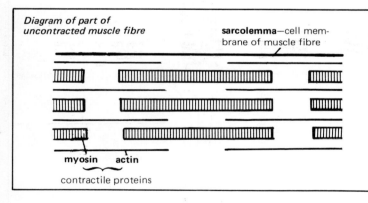

Diagram of part of uncontracted muscle fibre

sarcolemma—cell membrane of muscle fibre

myosin   actin
contractile proteins

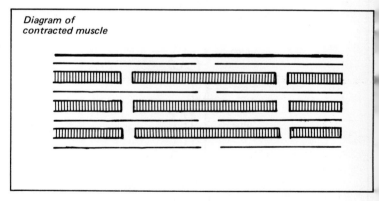

Diagram of contracted muscle

Lots of energy is needed for muscle contraction so reserves are stored as creatine phosphate—made by combining creatine with ATP:

creatine + ATP → ADP + creatine phosphate → ATP + creatine
(stored in muscle) (when energy needed)

Skeletal muscles usually work in antagonistic pairs i.e. they are arranged so that they have opposing effects to each other. Muscles cannot expand—they rely on the opposing muscle to return the bones to their original position.

The point of anchorage of a muscle is the origin.

The other end, attached to a bone which moves, is called the insertion.

A strain = overstretching of a muscle.
Cramp = sudden, involuntary and painful contraction of muscles.

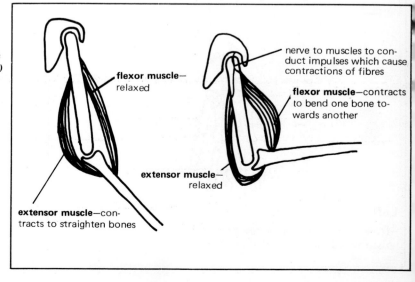

nerve to muscles to conduct impulses which cause contractions of fibres

flexor muscle—relaxed

flexor muscle—contracts to bend one bone towards another

extensor muscle—relaxed

extensor muscle—contracts to straighten bones

Muscles

Main muscles of right arm

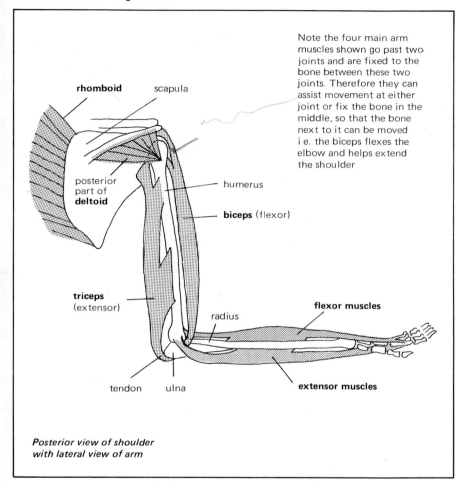

Note the four main arm muscles shown go past two joints and are fixed to the bone between these two joints. Therefore they can assist movement at either joint or fix the bone in the middle, so that the bone next to it can be moved i e. the biceps flexes the elbow and helps extend the shoulder

rhomboid

scapula

posterior part of **deltoid**

humerus

biceps (flexor)

triceps (extensor)

radius

flexor muscles

tendon

ulna

extensor muscles

Posterior view of shoulder with lateral view of arm

Main muscles of leg

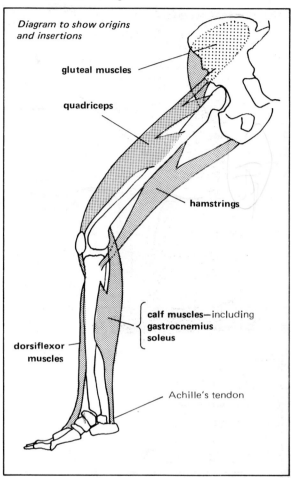

Diagram to show origins and insertions

gluteal muscles

quadriceps

hamstrings

calf muscles—including **gastrocnemius soleus**

dorsiflexor muscles

Achille's tendon

Only the larger muscles have been shown. There are many others which are responsible for rotating the limbs etc.

The pull of muscles in limbs is made more efficient by the use of pulley-like mechanisms e.g. at knee joint:

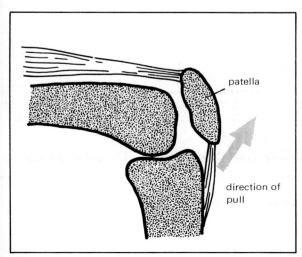

patella

direction of pull

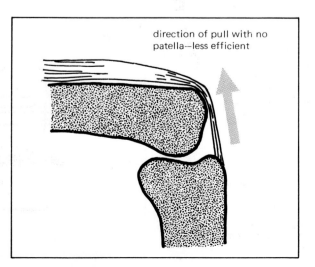

direction of pull with no patella—less efficient

Joints

These are where two bones come together.

1. Immovable joints

No movement between bones.

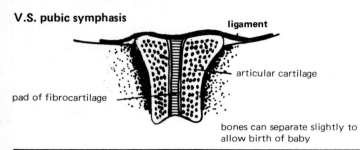

two bones of skull

bones interlock so don't pull apart

suture joint

V.S. suture

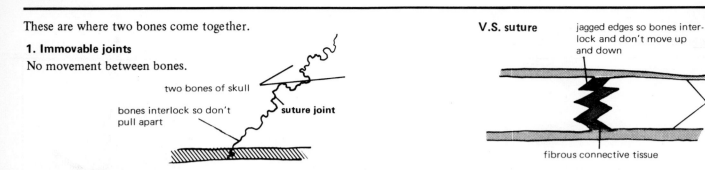

jagged edges so bones interlock and don't move up and down

periosteum

fibrous connective tissue

2. Slightly movable/cartilage joints

Limited movement between bones.

V.S. pubic symphasis

ligament

articular cartilage

pad of fibrocartilage

bones can separate slightly to allow birth of baby

V.S. joint between centra

centra of vertebrae

intervertebral disc of fibrocartilage—shock absorber

3. Fully movable/synovial joints

Lot of movement permitted. Many mechanisms to cut down friction.

Basic synovial joint

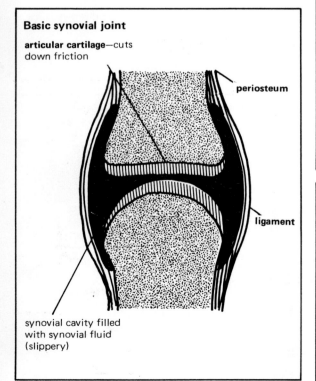

articular cartilage—cuts down friction

periosteum

ligament

synovial cavity filled with synovial fluid (slippery)

Hinge joint

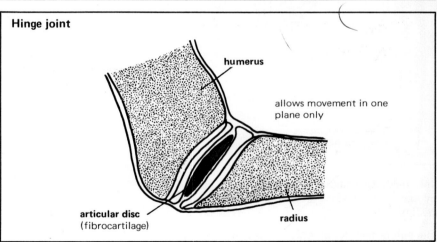

humerus

allows movement in one plane only

articular disc (fibrocartilage)

radius

Ball and socket joint
(acetabular cavity)

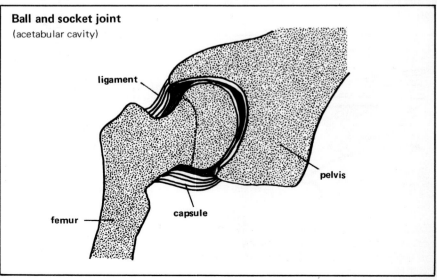

ligament

pelvis

femur

capsule

Arthritis—degeneration and infection of articular cartilage, ligaments and bone.

Gout—salts deposited in joint causing friction and wear of cartilage.

Bones as levers

People often use what scientists call levers to make work easier. Bones of the body also work like levers. There are three main orders of levers:

the effort can be in either direction. The position of the fulcrum determines the order of lever

A. First order
There are few levers of this type in the body.

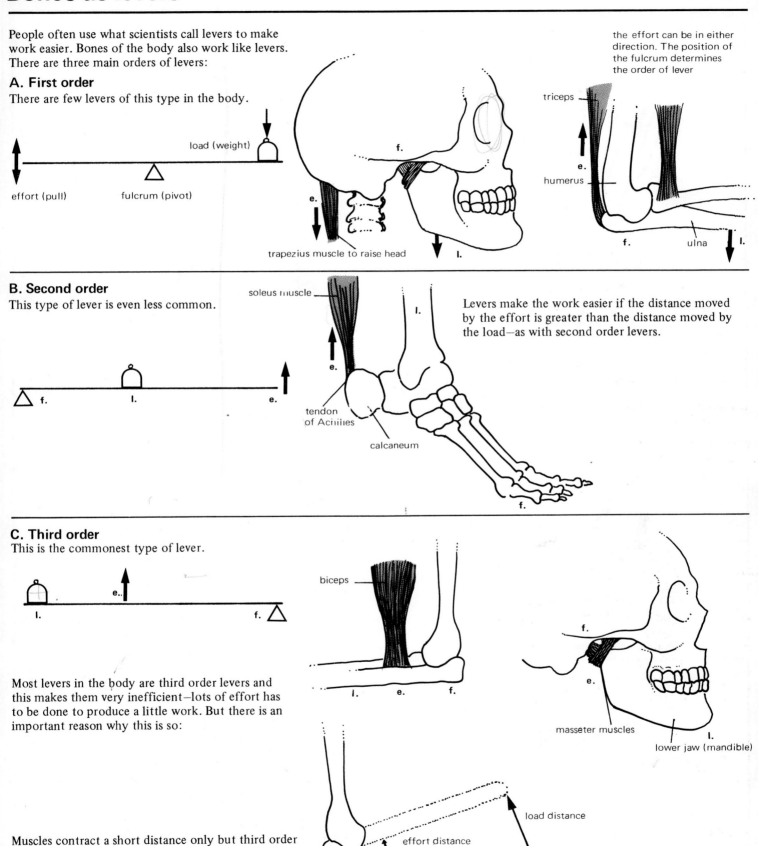

B. Second order
This type of lever is even less common.

Levers make the work easier if the distance moved by the effort is greater than the distance moved by the load—as with second order levers.

C. Third order
This is the commonest type of lever.

Most levers in the body are third order levers and this makes them very inefficient—lots of effort has to be done to produce a little work. But there is an important reason why this is so:

Muscles contract a short distance only but third order levers mean that the other end of the bone (load distance) moves a lot. Limbs etc. are therefore very mobile.

Control of muscles

V.S. motor end plate

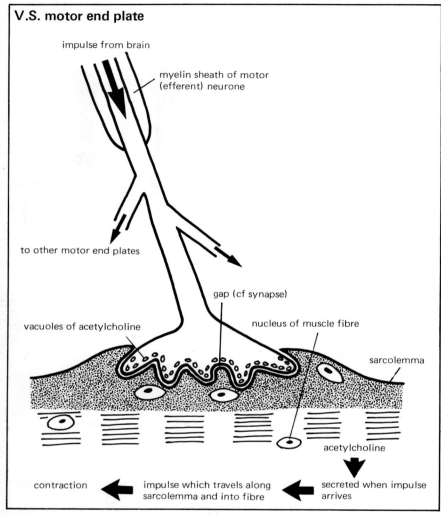

impulse from brain

myelin sheath of motor (efferent) neurone

to other motor end plates

gap (cf synapse)

nucleus of muscle fibre

vacuoles of acetylcholine

sarcolemma

acetylcholine

contraction ← impulse which travels along sarcolemma and into fibre ← secreted when impulse arrives

Motor end plates and proprioceptors work together so that muscles of the body contract in a smooth, controlled manner:

When the muscle is contracted to the correct tension, the central nervous system sends out no more impulses so no further contraction occurs. The correct tension is called muscle tone.

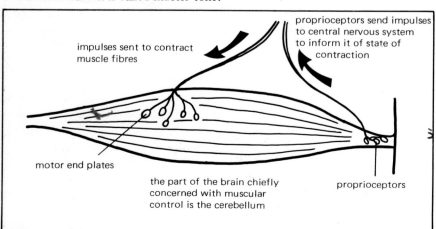

impulses sent to contract muscle fibres

proprioceptors send impulses to central nervous system to inform it of state of contraction

motor end plates

the part of the brain chiefly concerned with muscular control is the cerebellum

proprioceptors

Proprioceptors or stretch receptors

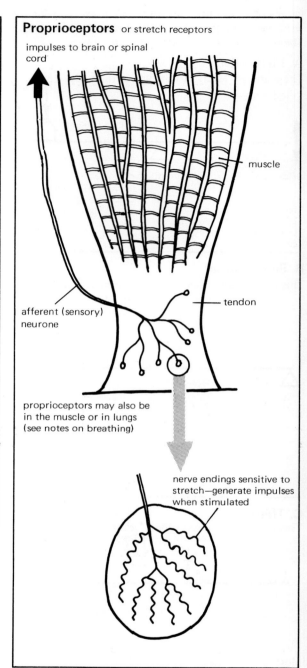

impulses to brain or spinal cord

muscle

afferent (sensory) neurone

tendon

proprioceptors may also be in the muscle or in lungs (see notes on breathing)

nerve endings sensitive to stretch—generate impulses when stimulated

Frequency of impulses to muscles

a One impulse to a muscle causes a twitch—muscle contracts, then relaxes e.g. blinking of eye.

b Several impulses at fairly long intervals causes spasms—muscle alternately contracts and partly relaxes.

c Many impulses at short time intervals cause tetanus—muscle remains contracted. Therefore to keep a muscle contracted, the central nervous system must send out impulses all the time.

N.B. Tetanus of muscles is not to be confused with the disease called "lockjaw."

Maintaining a good posture

Opposing muscles of the body are kept at different tensions, using proprioceptors (see previous notes) to keep the body in desired positions. Stresses on the muscles, skeleton etc. can be reduced if good positions are maintained—making sure the weight of the body is distributed evenly either side of the centre of gravity (c. of g.). Muscle tone is the term given to the slight contraction of muscles to maintain posture.

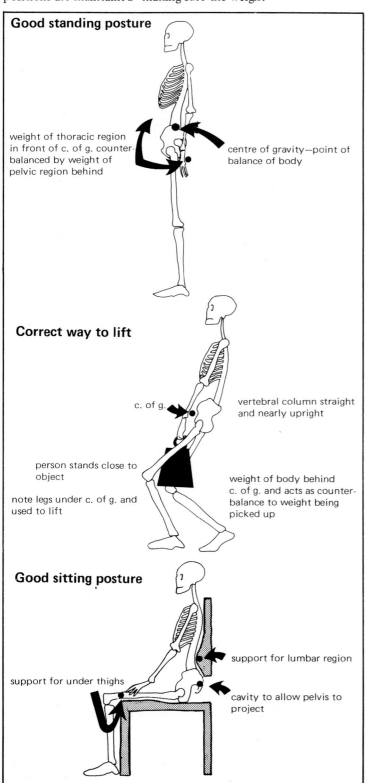

Good standing posture

weight of thoracic region in front of c. of g. counter-balanced by weight of pelvic region behind

centre of gravity—point of balance of body

Correct way to lift

c. of g.

vertebral column straight and nearly upright

person stands close to object

note legs under c. of g. and used to lift

weight of body behind c. of g. and acts as counter-balance to weight being picked up

Good sitting posture

support for under thighs

support for lumbar region

cavity to allow pelvis to project

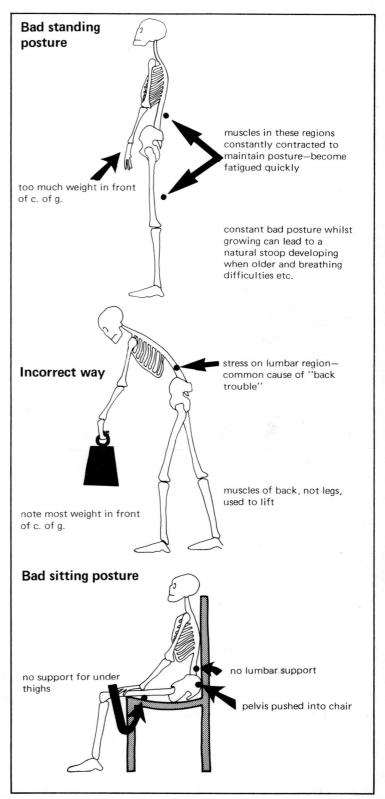

Bad standing posture

too much weight in front of c. of g.

muscles in these regions constantly contracted to maintain posture—become fatigued quickly

constant bad posture whilst growing can lead to a natural stoop developing when older and breathing difficulties etc.

Incorrect way

stress on lumbar region—common cause of "back trouble"

note most weight in front of c. of g.

muscles of back, not legs, used to lift

Bad sitting posture

no support for under thighs

no lumbar support

pelvis pushed into chair

Viruses

Healthy person—metabolism efficient and normal; free from diseases/malfunctioning.

Hygiene—actions whose aim is to preserve good health and prevent the spread of disease.

Most diseases are caused by micro-organisms or "germs"—usually viruses or bacteria.

Structure

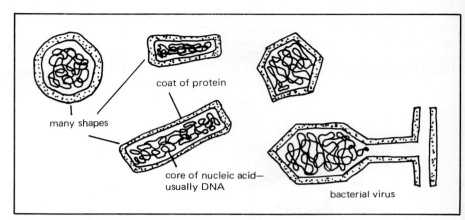

many shapes

coat of protein

core of nucleic acid— usually DNA

bacterial virus

Viruses can only reproduce in suitable, living cells. They do not feed but their nucleic acid takes over the metabolism of the host cell and causes it to make new viruses:—

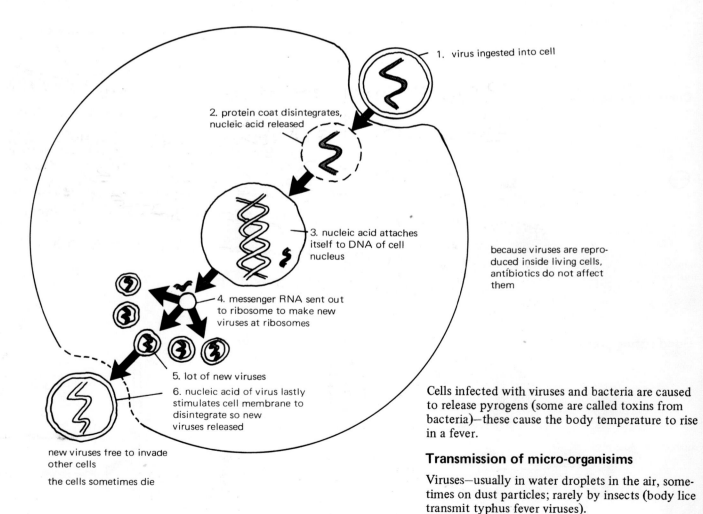

1. virus ingested into cell

2. protein coat disintegrates, nucleic acid released

3. nucleic acid attaches itself to DNA of cell nucleus

4. messenger RNA sent out to ribosome to make new viruses at ribosomes

5. lot of new viruses

6. nucleic acid of virus lastly stimulates cell membrane to disintegrate so new viruses released

new viruses free to invade other cells

the cells sometimes die

because viruses are repro- duced inside living cells, antibiotics do not affect them

Cells infected with viruses and bacteria are caused to release pyrogens (some are called toxins from bacteria)—these cause the body temperature to rise in a fever.

Transmission of micro-organisims

Viruses—usually in water droplets in the air, some- times on dust particles; rarely by insects (body lice transmit typhus fever viruses).

Bacteria—usually on dust particles or water droplets in the air; may be carried by insects (see later for details).

Bacteria

Typical bacterium

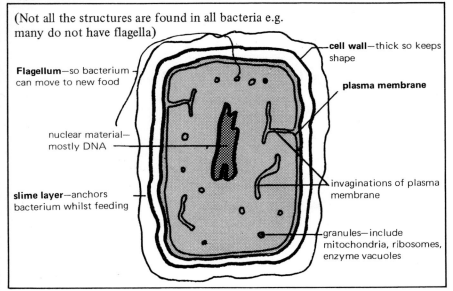

(Not all the structures are found in all bacteria e.g. many do not have flagella)

Flagellum—so bacterium can move to new food

nuclear material—mostly DNA

slime layer—anchors bacterium whilst feeding

cell wall—thick so keeps shape

plasma membrane

invaginations of plasma membrane

granules—include mitochondria, ribosomes, enzyme vacuoles

Shapes of bacteria

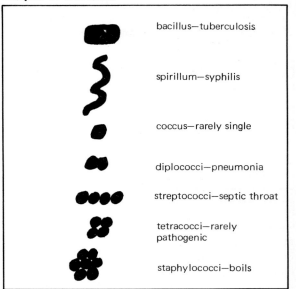

bacillus—tuberculosis

spirillum—syphilis

coccus—rarely single

diplococci—pneumonia

streptococci—septic throat

tetracocci—rarely pathogenic

staphylococci—boils

Feeding

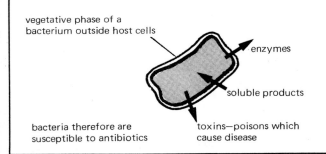

vegetative phase of a bacterium outside host cells

enzymes

soluble products

bacteria therefore are susceptible to antibiotics

toxins—poisons which cause disease

Bacteria feed outside of cells—in the intercellular fluid (lymph and plasma). They feed and grow best, and therefore multiply quickest in the following conditions:-

1. warmth—about 37° C best
2. moisture—needed so enzymes can act
3. darkness—ultra-violet light destroys them
4. specific food present—each bacterium needs a specific food substance. Each can feed on one kind of tissue only.

Results of growth

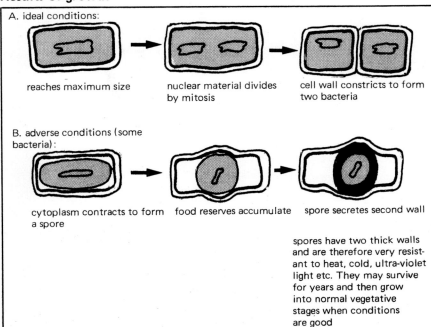

A. ideal conditions:

reaches maximum size

nuclear material divides by mitosis

cell wall constricts to form two bacteria

B. adverse conditions (some bacteria):

cytoplasm contracts to form a spore

food reserves accumulate

spore secretes second wall

spores have two thick walls and are therefore very resistant to heat, cold, ultra-violet light etc. They may survive for years and then grow into normal vegetative stages when conditions are good

Growth curve of bacteria in a culture

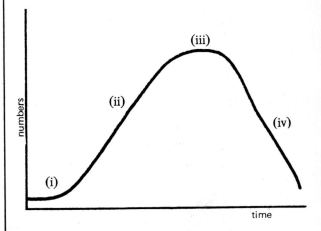

numbers

time

(i) lag phase—bacteria synthesise enzymes but do not reproduce
(ii) log phase—bacteria grow and divide at constant, maximum rate
(iii) stationary phase—the toxins released by bacteria cause them to stop growing
(iv) decline phase—more bacteria die than are reproduced. Eventually only spores are left.

Destroying bacteria

Antibiotics

Extracts of other micro-organisms (bacteria and fungi). Safe to inject. Some work by being mistaken for enzymes needed to make walls of bacteria:-

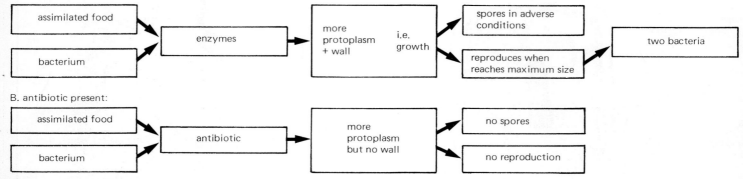

A. normally:

| assimilated food | | | spores in adverse conditions | |
| bacterium | enzymes | more protoplasm + wall i.e. growth | reproduces when reaches maximum size | two bacteria |

B. antibiotic present:

| assimilated food | | | no spores |
| bacterium | antibiotic | more protoplasm but no wall | no reproduction |

Many strains of bacteria are now able to distinguish between antibiotics and the enzymes so they no-longer take up the antibiotic by mistake—i.e. they are resistant to the antibiotic and another one must be used to destroy the bacteria.

Disinfectants

Kill vegetative and spore stages of pathogens. They may kill the living cells of man too, if they are swallowed. e.g. phenol, iodine, chlorine, formalin, sodium hypochlorite, murcurochrome

bacteria and spores

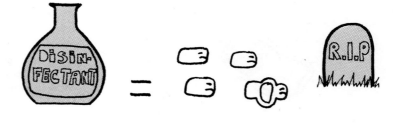

Antiseptics

Prevent pathogens feeding but do not kill spores. Less poisonous than disinfectants—many are weak solutions of disinfectants.

reproduces later to form many offspring

Sterilisation

Methods of killing all living organisms present—including all spores.

moist heat for 30 mins. at 116°C (in type of pressure cooker called an autoclave)

dry heat for 30 mins. at 160° C (in special type of oven)

formalin vapour
chlorine
sulphur dioxide

chemicals

e.g. gamma rays for sterilising disposable syringes

many eyedrops

oily eyedrops

process called fumigation

see disinfectants

The body's defences against pathogens

The body has means of preventing pathogens (disease-causing organisms) entering the blood system and being circulated:

natural opening kept closed
except when being used:
mouth—lips
vagina—labia + hymen
anus
urethra } sphincter muscles
eustachian tube—valve

substances secreted to
protect exposed surfaces:
eyes—tears
ears—wax
lungs
vagina } mucus

Skin

epidermis prevents entry of
all pathogens whilst intact

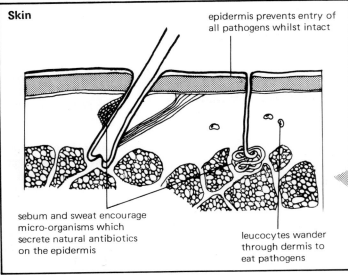

sebum and sweat encourage
micro-organisms which
secrete natural antibiotics
on the epidermis

leucocytes wander
through dermis to
eat pathogens

stomach secretes hydro-
chloric acid to kill most
bacteria eaten

If pathogens enter the body

1. leucocytes leave capillaries and lymphatic ducts to eat bacteria (see notes on blood)

2. if pathogens enter blood:

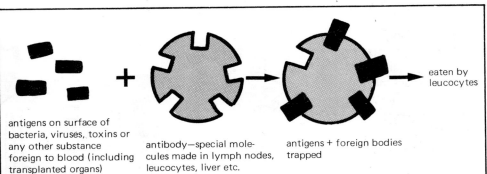

antigens on surface of
bacteria, viruses, toxins or
any other substance
foreign to blood (including
transplanted organs)

antibody—special mole-
cules made in lymph nodes,
leucocytes, liver etc.

antigens + foreign bodies
trapped

eaten by
leucocytes

Every new type of antigen has to have a new type of antibody made to neutralise it. A type of antibody, once made, remains circulating in the blood plasma so it is available for immediate use in the future.

3. If pathogens enter tissues on which they feed:

   a pyrogens released which affect body temperature control centre in the hypothalamus of
   brain—causes temperature to rise above best
   temperature for growth of pathogens (so
   growth slowed down)

   b cells die and then eaten by leucocytes

   c sometimes cysts form—connective tissue formed
   around infected cells to isolate them from rest
   of body.

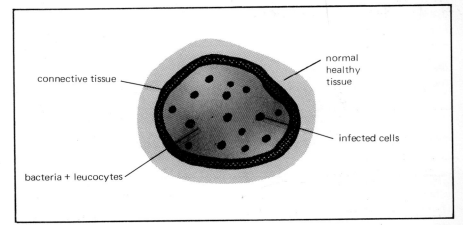

connective tissue

normal
healthy
tissue

bacteria + leucocytes

infected cells

Immunity

Phenomenon by which the body is protected from pathogens causing disease.

Natural immunity

The body is immune to some diseases without previous exposure to them. Possible mechanisms:

a immune to diseases of animals e.g. swine fever, fowl pest, as the body does not have correct food supply for those pathogens

b body sometimes inherits ability to produce antibodies without suffering from the disease e.g. many people immune to tuberculosis

Acquired immunity

The person's antibody-making mechanism is stimulated to make antibodies which may remain in the plasma for all life to protect body from disease

Acquired by suffering

Once the body has suffered from disease and produced antibodies, these usually remain available for rest of life (but will not protect from new strains of pathogens — e.g. there are about 50 strains of common cold virus so you can suffer from 50 colds and any other new strains which appear). Antibodies of chicken pox, German measles etc. protect from all future attacks.

Acquired by immunisation

Active immunity

Body deliberately infected with weakened or killed pathogens (or extracts).

Vaccines injected or given by mouth in progressively stronger doses till last injection stimulates production of antibodies which last for many years.

Booster injections are usually needed every few years.

Passive immunity

The person receives ready-made antibodies

a babies receive antibodies from their mother and these protect them from diseases for up to 12 months

b Antibodies extracted from serum of person or animal (usually a horse) which has recovered from the disease. The serum is used to treat a person suffering from the disease - it gives no long-term immunity.

Usual programme of vaccination

Disease	Time of vaccination	Time of booster
diphtheria tetanus whooping cough	3 injections - usually at 6, 8, 14 months	before starting school (as risk of infection greater)
poliomyelitis	3 oral (Sabin) doses as above	as above and on leaving school
measles	12 months	none needed
german measles	before puberty (girls only)	none needed
tuberculosis	13 years	none needed

other vaccines are available for people likely to come into contact with smallpox, cholera, typhoid, rabies, yellow fever etc.

Infectious diseases

These are caused by micro-organisms which live off human tissues causing:

A Fever—see previous notes on body's defences

B Destruction of cells by micro-organisms feeding on them or toxins destroy them or leucocytes eat infected cells

C Production of antibodies to counteract the pathogens—usually takes about 2 weeks

The pathogens feed and reproduce millions of offspring. Some offspring leave the body through:

i Natural openings—especially with expired air (in water droplets) or with faeces.

ii Wounds made by ectoparasitic insects feeding e.g. fleas, lice, mosquitoes (see later). The pathogens can therefore enter another, healthy person and cause the disease in his body either with food/air he needs or when the insects feed on him.

	Disease	How enters body	Usual tissues infected	Usual results (other than fever)
Viruses	1. chicken pox	inspired or contact with infected articles	blood and skin	spots
	2. common cold	as for 1.	mucous membranes of respiratory organs	inflammation; lot of mucus
	3. German measles	as for 1.	skin, respiratory organs	rash; swollen glands
	4. influenza	inspired	as for 2 or gut or nervous tissue	as for 2 + aching
	5. measles	as for 1.	as for 3	as for 3 + swollen eyes
	6. mumps	as for 4.	salivary glands	swelling
	7. poliomyelitis	with infected food/water	gut, spinal cord	paralysis
	8. smallpox	inspired or contact with infected person	blood, skin	spots → scars
	9. typhus fever	lice or fleas biting	blood, skin	severe fever, aching
Bacteria	10. diphtheria	as for 8.	throat, blood, heart, nerves	severe fever
	11. summer diarrhoea	with infected food	gut	diarrhoea
	12. tuberculosis	with milk or inspired	lungs, bones	tissues destroyed
	13. typhoid fever	with food or water	gut	diarrhoea, cramps
	14. whooping cough	as for 1.	bronchioles	recurrent cough
Others	15. amoebic dysentery	with infected water	colon	severe diarrhoea, blood loss
	16. malaria	bite of mosquito	blood, liver	anaemia, severe fever
	17. ringworm	contact with infected skin or articles	skin, hair	itching, baldness

Different syllabuses require students to know a few of the above diseases including methods of transmission. The diseases usually include viral and bacterial diseases transmitted by insects.

Carriers of disease

Insects and their allies (ticks and mites) are important carriers of disease as they can move from one person to another or from infected substances (e.g. in dustbins) to food which is later eaten.

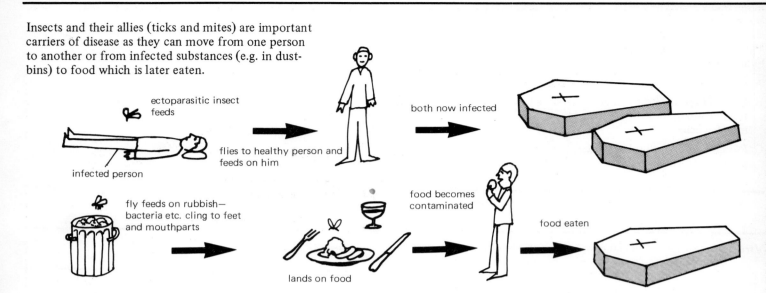

ectoparasitic insect feeds

infected person

flies to healthy person and feeds on him

both now infected

fly feeds on rubbish— bacteria etc. cling to feet and mouthparts

lands on food

food becomes contaminated

food eaten

Life cycle of body louse

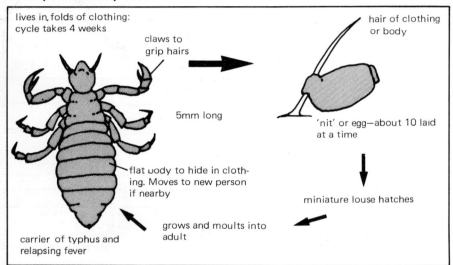

lives in, folds of clothing: cycle takes 4 weeks

claws to grip hairs

5mm long

flat body to hide in clothing. Moves to new person if nearby

carrier of typhus and relapsing fever

grows and moults into adult

hair of clothing or body

'nit' or egg—about 10 laid at a time

miniature louse hatches

Bed bug

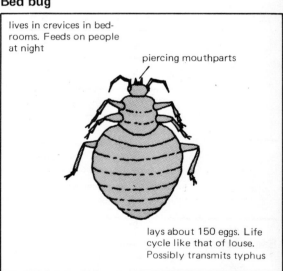

lives in crevices in bedrooms. Feeds on people at night

piercing mouthparts

lays about 150 eggs. Life cycle like that of louse. Possibly transmits typhus

Itchmite

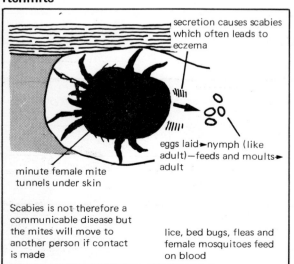

secretion causes scabies which often leads to eczema

minute female mite tunnels under skin

eggs laid→nymph (like adult)—feeds and moults→adult

Scabies is not therefore a communicable disease but the mites will move to another person if contact is made

lice, bed bugs, fleas and female mosquitoes feed on blood

Flea

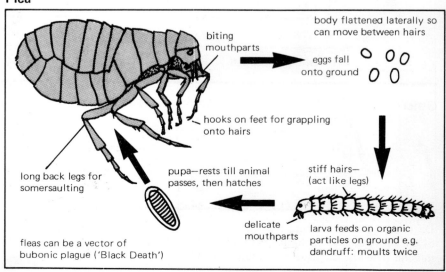

biting mouthparts

body flattened laterally so can move between hairs

eggs fall onto ground

hooks on feet for grappling onto hairs

long back legs for somersaulting

pupa—rests till animal passes, then hatches

delicate mouthparts

stiff hairs— (act like legs)

larva feeds on organic particles on ground e.g. dandruff: moults twice

fleas can be a vector of bubonic plague ('Black Death')

Controlling vectors

If the life cycle of the vector transmitting the disease
is known, it is much easier to keep it under control.
Two examples are given below.

House-fly

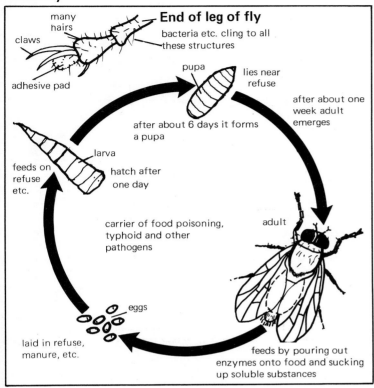

many hairs

claws

adhesive pad

End of leg of fly

bacteria etc. cling to all these structures

pupa

lies near refuse

after about one week adult emerges

after about 6 days it forms a pupa

larva

hatch after one day

feeds on refuse etc.

carrier of food poisoning, typhoid and other pathogens

adult

eggs

laid in refuse, manure, etc.

feeds by pouring out enzymes onto food and sucking up soluble substances

Mosquito

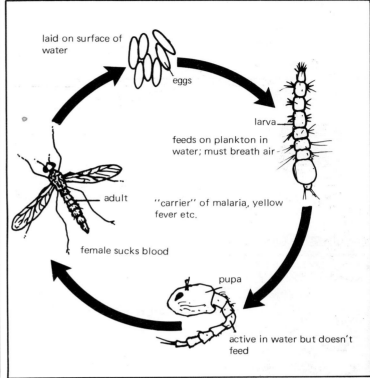

laid on surface of water

eggs

larva

feeds on plankton in water; must breath air

adult

"carrier" of malaria, yellow fever etc.

female sucks blood

pupa

active in water but doesn't feed

The most vulnerable stages of the life cycles. i.e. the
stages where lots of insects can be controlled easily
are:

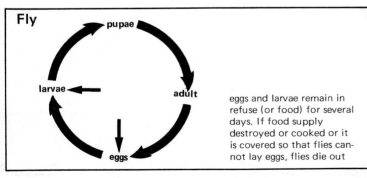

Fly

pupae

larvae

adult

eggs

eggs and larvae remain in
refuse (or food) for several
days. If food supply
destroyed or cooked or it
is covered so that flies cannot lay eggs, flies die out

Mosquito

eggs

adult

larvae

pupae

larvae and pupae aquatic
so if water sprayed with
insecticide, killed. Oil
sprayed onto surface will
also prevent them breathing

There are many reasons for cooking food:

1. Destroying pathogens, eggs of carriers and other
unwanted animals.

2. Food is made more digestible—some large molecules are broken down e.g starches.

3. Food becomes softer—fibres of meat and vegetables
become separated.

4. Some flavours are developed—probably as a result
of all the above reasons.

5. Different ways of cooking mean that food can be
presented in different ways.

But there are disadvantages in cooking food:

1. Heat destroys some vitamins e.g. vitamins B1, C.

2. Some vitamins and minerals dissolve in the water
used for cooking (this should therefore be used to
make sauces, gravies etc.).

3. Softer food means that pathogens breed more
quickly—cooked food must therefore be protected.

4. Teeth and gums have less work to do when masti-
cating (chewing) cooked food so the gums become
softer and allow dental decay to proceed more
rapidly.

Food poisoning

Caused by eating	Symptoms	Effect of cooking	Usual means of Infection
1. Poisonous food eaten by mistake	various—depends on substance eaten	usually no effect on substance	fungi, berries, laburnum seeds, etc.
2. Contaminated food	various	usually no effect	sewage contaminated food; chemicals added during manufacture
3. Food from diseased animal	various	usually destroys pathogens	cysts of tapeworms in meat, infected milk
4. *Salmonellae* bacilli which grow and multiply in gut and secrete toxins	cause typhoid and other fevers—see previous notes. Several hours elapse before symptoms appear as toxins have to be made	slowly kills bacteria	from faeces of rodents or man. Transmitted by flies or unhygienic person. Bacteria grow and multiply rapidly on animal products—meat, pastes, artificial cream, egg products etc.
5. *Staphylococci* bacteria feed on food and secrete toxins (which are then eaten)	severe vomiting and diarrhoea. Symptoms appear about 4 hours after eating food	slowly destroys toxins	septic finger touching food or person with nose or throat infection coughing onto food—especially meat and meat products
6. *Clostridium welchii* grow and multiply in gut	often mild abdominal cramps, diarrhoea. May be severe. Symptoms 8-24 hours after eating food	very slowly kills spores	Bacteria do not need oxygen so they often breed in precooked meat—even in tins (unless contents sterile)
7. *Clostridium botulinum* feed on food and excrete toxin	headache, dizziness, fatigue, paralysis of muscles. Death common. Symptoms usually in 1-2 days	quickly destroys toxin. Slowly destroys spores.	as for C. welchii but especially in home-preserved foods (not fruit or vegetables)

Note that common sources of food poisoning by bacteria are meat and egg products as the bacteria will also be able to feed off man (= meat!). These foods must not be left exposed to the air in a warm place after being cooked as the bacteria will breed very quickly—many bacteria can complete their life cycle in less than one hour.

Food preservation

Methods of preventing micro-organisms growing on food so that it may be stored for long periods of time and still be fit for human consumption.

1 Raising the osmotic pressure of the food by sugar (syrup) or salt. This prevents bacteria etc. growing as they become dehydrated.

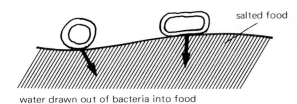

salted food

water drawn out of bacteria into food

2 Pickling in alcohol or vinegar kills all vegetative stages of bacteria and even the spores cannot germinate and feed.

spore germinates but dies

alcohol/vinegar enters and destroys protoplasm

3 Drying/dehydrating removes most of the water from food so the bacteria cannot feed or grow (see notes on the conditions bacteria need to grow). Chemical preservatives are sometimes added (e.g. sulphur dioxide, benzoic acid) to lessen the risk of bacteria growing if the food becomes damp.

4 Canning sterilises the food—i.e. kills all organisms present and prevents the entry of further bacteria etc.

a fresh food taken, prepared and placed in sealed cans
b heat all food to about $125°$ C for about 15 minutes
c cool rapidly (produces a partial vacuum in can)

5 Deep-freezing by *quickly* lowering the temperature to about $-40°$ C prevents bacteria growing but *does not kill* bacteria. Note that:

a If food thawed out, the bacteria present will immediately begin feeding and growing. Frozen foods must therefore be eaten soon after thawing.

b Enzymes in food are just active at cold temperatures so frozen foods will not keep indefinitely.

c Fresh vegetables and fruit are blanched before freezing—placed in boiling water for a few seconds to destroy most enzymes—reduces tainting by enzymes digesting the food and therefore prolongs storage life.

6 Freeze drying:

a Food prepared (cooked if necessary).
b Quickly frozen as for 5.—so ice crystals do not form inside cells and pierce the walls causing the food to go mushy when thawed.
c Placed in vacuum chamber where ice sublimes (vaporises into water vapour direct with no intermediate water stage).
d Packed in waterproof packets. Quickly returns to original shape and texture if hot water added.

Milk

1. Pasteurisation. Milk heated to $63\text{-}66°$ C for 30 minutes or $72°$ C for 15 seconds and then cooled quickly to $10°$ C. Kills most vegetative bacteria including those which cause tuberculosis.

2. UHT (Ultra Heat Treated). Milk heated to $132°$C for 1 second and so is sterilised. Sterile containers are filled under aseptic conditions and then sealed so they are airtight.

7 Radiating food with gamma rays sterilises it (see notes on sterilising). New methods of preserving food are being developed using this phenomenon.

Personal hygiene

Much can be done to keep the body healthy. A healthy body stimulates self-confidence and a generally well-balanced mental attitude.

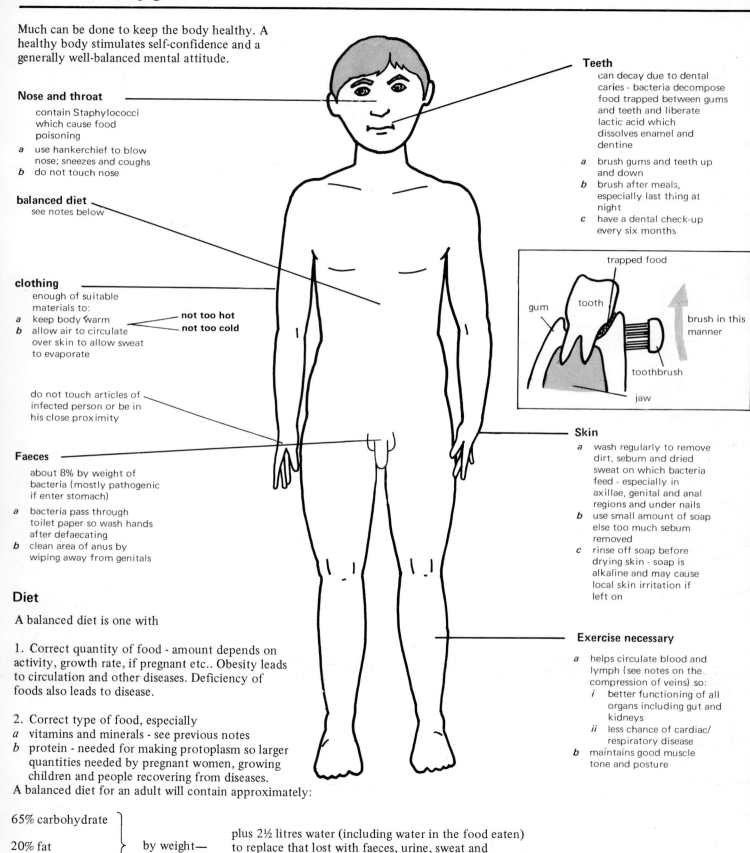

Nose and throat

contain Staphylococci which cause food poisoning

a use hankerchief to blow nose; sneezes and coughs
b do not touch nose

balanced diet

see notes below

clothing

enough of suitable materials to:
a keep body warm
b allow air to circulate over skin to allow sweat to evaporate

not too hot
not too cold

do not touch articles of infected person or be in his close proximity

Faeces

about 8% by weight of bacteria (mostly pathogenic if enter stomach)

a bacteria pass through toilet paper so wash hands after defaecating
b clean area of anus by wiping away from genitals

Teeth

can decay due to dental caries - bacteria decompose food trapped between gums and teeth and liberate lactic acid which dissolves enamel and dentine

a brush gums and teeth up and down
b brush after meals, especially last thing at night
c have a dental check-up every six months

trapped food

gum   tooth

brush in this manner

toothbrush

jaw

Skin

a wash regularly to remove dirt, sebum and dried sweat on which bacteria feed - especially in axillae, genital and anal regions and under nails
b use small amount of soap else too much sebum removed
c rinse off soap before drying skin - soap is alkaline and may cause local skin irritation if left on

Exercise necessary

a helps circulate blood and lymph (see notes on the compression of veins) so:
  i better functioning of all organs including gut and kidneys
  ii less chance of cardiac/respiratory disease
b maintains good muscle tone and posture

Diet

A balanced diet is one with

1. Correct quantity of food - amount depends on activity, growth rate, if pregnant etc.. Obesity leads to circulation and other diseases. Deficiency of foods also leads to disease.

2. Correct type of food, especially
a vitamins and minerals - see previous notes
b protein - needed for making protoplasm so larger quantities needed by pregnant women, growing children and people recovering from diseases.

A balanced diet for an adult will contain approximately:

65% carbohydrate ⎫
20% fat   ⎬ by weight—   plus 2½ litres water (including water in the food eaten) to replace that lost with faeces, urine, sweat and expired air
15% protein   ⎭

Domestic hygiene

Proper planning of houses can do much to reduce the chance of infection of the occupants. The main areas which affect health are sewage disposal, (this must be separate from living/eating accommodation and with a supply of hot water for washing), and food preparation. Below are examples of badly-designed and well-designed kitchens.

Poor design

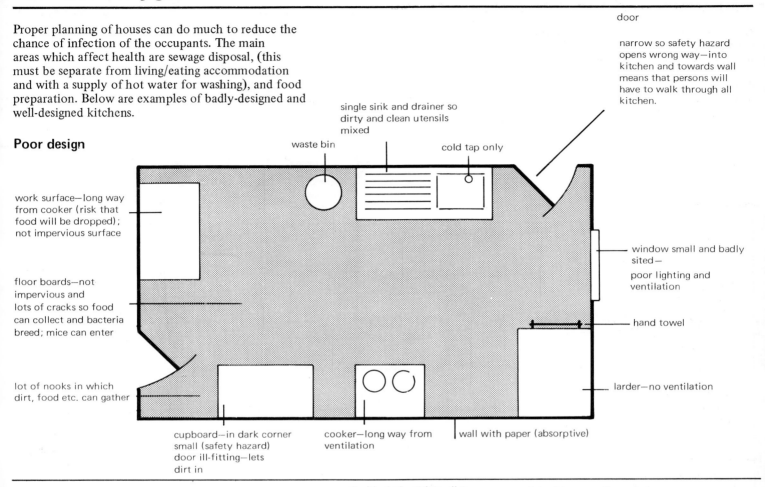

door

narrow so safety hazard opens wrong way—into kitchen and towards wall means that persons will have to walk through all kitchen.

single sink and drainer so dirty and clean utensils mixed

waste bin

cold tap only

work surface—long way from cooker (risk that food will be dropped); not impervious surface

floor boards—not impervious and lots of cracks so food can collect and bacteria breed; mice can enter

lot of nooks in which dirt, food etc. can gather

window small and badly sited—

poor lighting and ventilation

hand towel

larder—no ventilation

cupboard—in dark corner small (safety hazard) door ill-fitting—lets dirt in

cooker—long way from ventilation

wall with paper (absorptive)

Good design

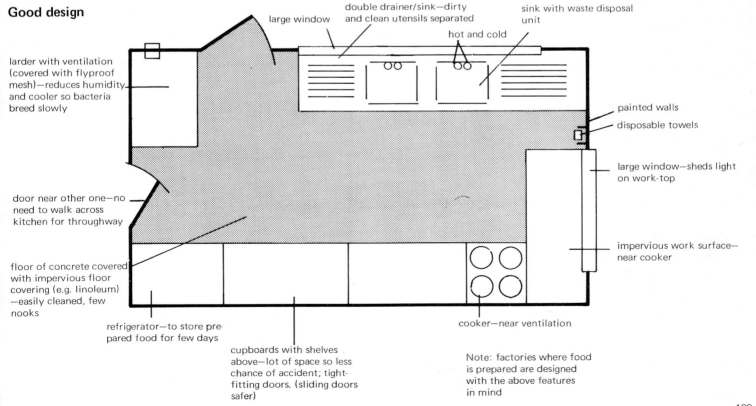

large window

double drainer/sink—dirty and clean utensils separated

sink with waste disposal unit

hot and cold

larder with ventilation (covered with flyproof mesh)—reduces humidity and cooler so bacteria breed slowly

painted walls

disposable towels

large window—sheds light on work-top

door near other one—no need to walk across kitchen for throughway

impervious work surface—near cooker

floor of concrete covered with impervious floor covering (e.g. linoleum)—easily cleaned, few nooks

refrigerator—to store prepared food for few days

cupboards with shelves above—lot of space so less chance of accident; tight-fitting doors. (sliding doors safer)

cooker—near ventilation

Note: factories where food is prepared are designed with the above features in mind

The public health inspector (Environmental health officer)

Responsible to committees of Local Authorities (e.g. Health Committee). His duties are to ensure that laws concerned with public welfare are enforced, especially to prevent communicable diseases spreading, chiefly by:

1. Keeping carriers of disease under control.
2. Ensuring uncontaminated water supply.
3. Ensuring efficient sanitation.
4. Checking that all food sold is wholesome.
5. Preventing hazardous working and living conditions.

His main duties:

Housing	Household supplies	Factories

Housing

1. fit for habitation
2. enough air space for new houses
3. prevent overcrowding
4. hotels have hygienic kitchens etc.
5. ridding of vermin (call in expert)
6. disinfect clothing etc. of persons with contagious diseases

Household supplies

1. wells, pumps etc. provide water fit for consumption
2. sewage disposal efficient
3. rubbish tips properly constructed and not harbouring vermin
4. imported food and carcases wholesome
5. food in shops, cafes etc. fit for sale
6. sample milk on floats to ensure uncontaminated

Factories

1. warehouses etc. free from pests and vermin
2. food hygiene regulations observed
3. enough space/toilets for workers
4. workers have protective clothing if necessary
5. no air pollution from chimneys
6. no excessive noise emitted

Food hygiene regulations

Statutory requirements for factories, shops etc. where food is handled. The Public Health Inspectors ensure these are carried out and can advise Local Authorities to prosecute if necessary.

A Premises must be well lit, ventilated, clean, well-designed so little chance of contamination e.g. toilets must not lead directly from room where food handled.

B Sanitary facilities must be adequate:
  i adequate washing facilities with nail brushes, clean towels etc.
  ii waterproof dressings available to cover sores, cuts etc.
  iii separate place to keep outdoor clothing

C Equipment which contacts food must be:
  i clean and in good repair
  ii of non-absorbent material (e.g. stainless steel or plastic)
  iii containers and vehicles clean

D Food handlers:
  i must be clean and wear clean, protective clothing
  ii no smoking or spitting
  iii cuts etc. must be covered with waterproof dressings

E In cafés etc:
  i meat, fish, gravy, imitation cream etc. must be stored at below 10°C or above 63°C so pathogens do not breed quickly
  ii cooked meats on display must be in refrigerated windows.

There are other regulations for the supply of milk, drugs, ice-cream, meat etc.

Water supply

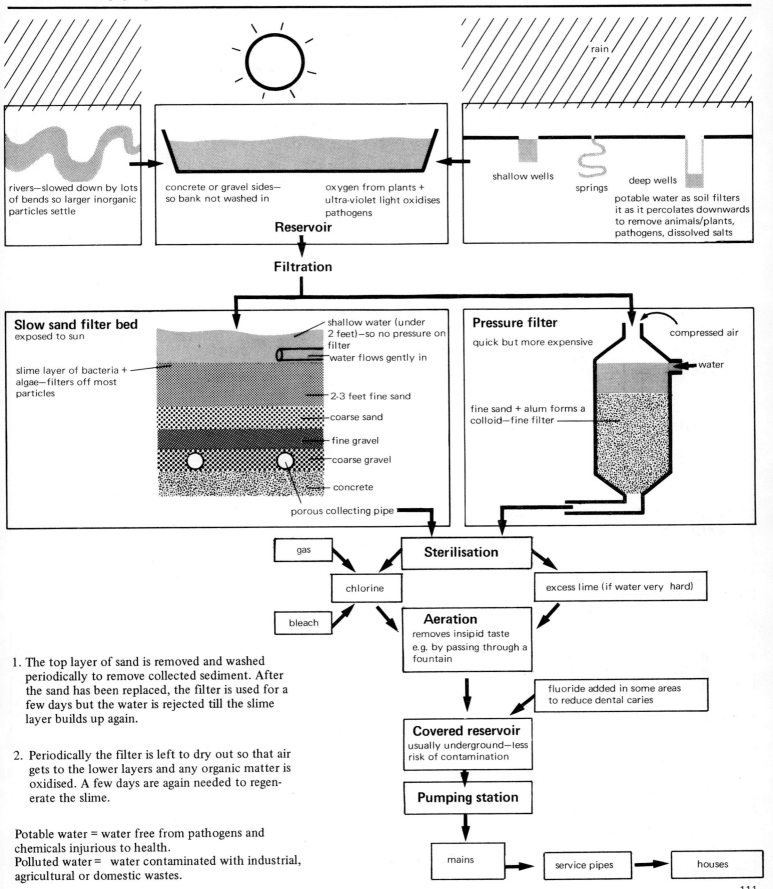

rivers—slowed down by lots of bends so larger inorganic particles settle

concrete or gravel sides—so bank not washed in

oxygen from plants + ultra-violet light oxidises pathogens

Reservoir

rain

shallow wells

springs

deep wells

potable water as soil filters it as it percolates downwards to remove animals/plants, pathogens, dissolved salts

Filtration

Slow sand filter bed
exposed to sun

slime layer of bacteria + algae—filters off most particles

shallow water (under 2 feet)—so no pressure on filter
water flows gently in

2-3 feet fine sand

coarse sand

fine gravel

coarse gravel

concrete

porous collecting pipe

Pressure filter

quick but more expensive

compressed air

water

fine sand + alum forms a colloid—fine filter

Sterilisation

gas

chlorine

bleach

excess lime (if water very hard)

Aeration
removes insipid taste e.g. by passing through a fountain

fluoride added in some areas to reduce dental caries

Covered reservoir
usually underground—less risk of contamination

Pumping station

mains

service pipes

houses

1. The top layer of sand is removed and washed periodically to remove collected sediment. After the sand has been replaced, the filter is used for a few days but the water is rejected till the slime layer builds up again.

2. Periodically the filter is left to dry out so that air gets to the lower layers and any organic matter is oxidised. A few days are again needed to regenerate the slime.

Potable water = water free from pathogens and chemicals injurious to health.
Polluted water = water contaminated with industrial, agricultural or domestic wastes.

Sewage treatment

This is similar to water purification as micro-organisms are responsible for decomposing unwanted organic matter. There are many methods:

1 . Conservancy methods

Sewage (chiefly excreta) collected in receptacles and the bacteria present slowly digest the faeces etc. The contents have to be emptied periodically.

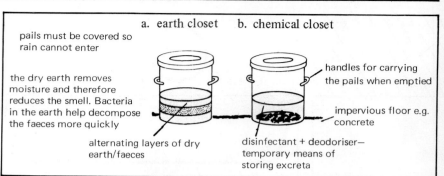

pails must be covered so rain cannot enter

a. earth closet   b. chemical closet

the dry earth removes moisture and therefore reduces the smell. Bacteria in the earth help decompose the faeces more quickly

handles for carrying the pails when emptied

impervious floor e.g. concrete

alternating layers of dry earth/faeces

disinfectant + deodoriser— temporary means of storing excreta

2. Water carriage methods

Domestic waste water and excreta are carried away in sewers so that they can be treated away from dwellings.

Cesspool   (modified conservancy method)
used in country areas where no sewage works is nearby

long, porous drains along which liquefied sewage slowly passes along and diffuses into soil (where bacteria digest it completely)

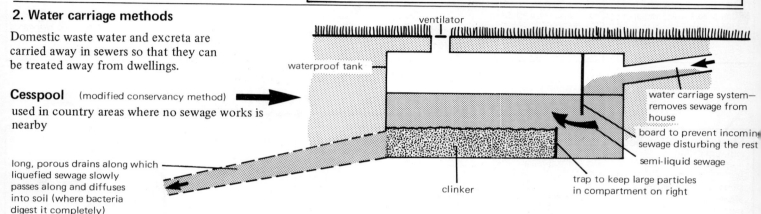

ventilator

waterproof tank

water carriage system— removes sewage from house

board to prevent incoming sewage disturbing the rest

semi-liquid sewage

clinker

trap to keep large particles in compartment on right

---

sewage works

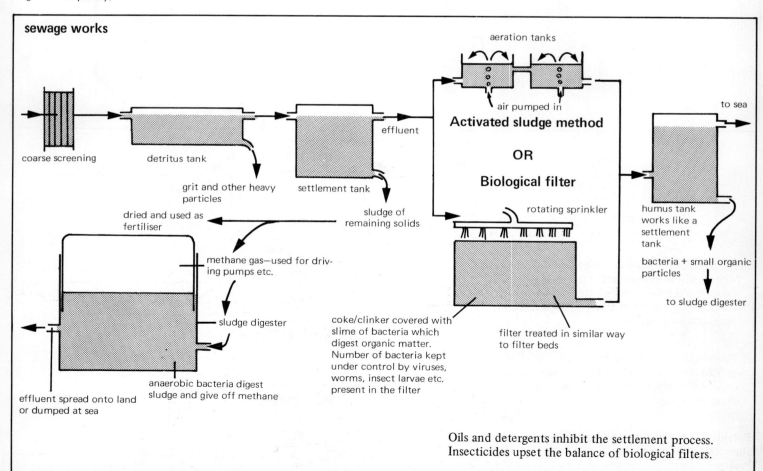

aeration tanks

air pumped in

Activated sludge method

OR

Biological filter

to sea

coarse screening

detritus tank

effluent

grit and other heavy particles

settlement tank

rotating sprinkler

humus tank works like a settlement tank

bacteria + small organic particles

to sludge digester

dried and used as fertiliser

sludge of remaining solids

methane gas—used for driving pumps etc.

sludge digester

coke/clinker covered with slime of bacteria which digest organic matter. Number of bacteria kept under control by viruses, worms, insect larvae etc. present in the filter

filter treated in similar way to filter beds

anaerobic bacteria digest sludge and give off methane

effluent spread onto land or dumped at sea

Oils and detergents inhibit the settlement process. Insecticides upset the balance of biological filters.

Sewage treatment

Slow sand filter under construction

- fine sand
- coarse sand
- gravel
- porous bricks
- tunnels—collect treated water
- sloping concrete floor— carries water to collecting pipes

Sewage treatment works

- sludge digesting tank
- biological filters
- clinker
- rotating sprinkler
- effluent

Addiction

An addict is someone who is compelled to take substances even though they may be harmful to him. The way addiction to smoking can start is summarised thus:

Smoking

Advantages—probably none (but see stage 2. on right)

Disadvantages—

a   expensive, messy, bad breath, stained teeth, poor taste/smell, litter problem
b   nausea and dizziness (at first)
c   nasal and throat mucous membranes irritated so lot of mucus secreted
d   paralyses cilia of respiratory passages leading to accumulation of mucus (must be coughed up)
e   nicotine absorbed into blood and constricts arteries causing high blood pressure—heart has more work to do and so suffers
f   digestion and peristalsis impeded—may irritate peptic ulcers
g   hydrocarbons in tar cause cancer
h   pregnant women who smoke have smaller (and hence weaker) babies

Excess alcohol

a   thinking slowed down—poor concentration and co-ordination, slow reactions, judgements, inhibitions affected
b   nausea, vomiting, headache
c   loss of appetite leading to unbalanced diet and possible cirrhosis of liver
d   delirium coma death (sometimes)

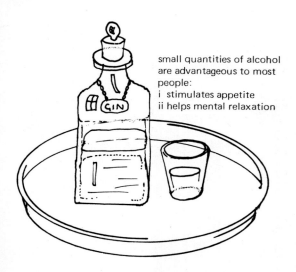

small quantities of alcohol are advantageous to most people:
i   stimulates appetite
ii helps mental relaxation

Addiction is very difficult to overcome but must involve reconditioning the body's metabolism so it can do without the addictive substance.

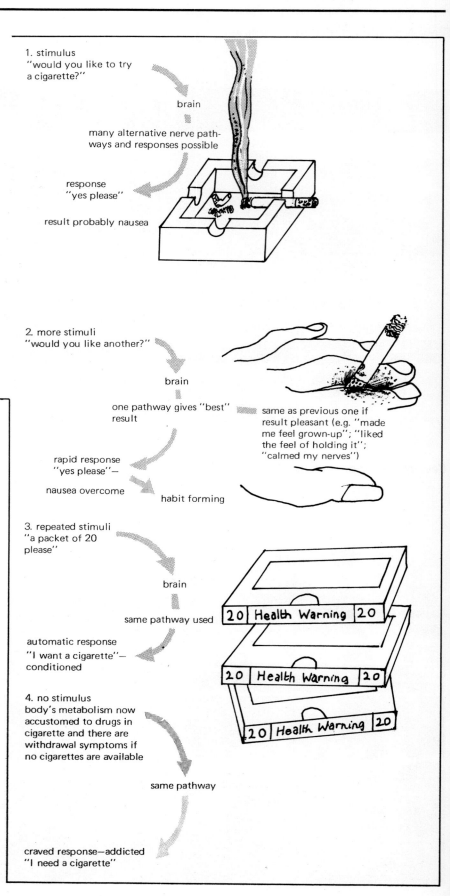

1. stimulus
"would you like to try a cigarette?"

brain

many alternative nerve pathways and responses possible

response
"yes please"

result probably nausea

2. more stimuli
"would you like another?"

brain

one pathway gives "best" result

rapid response
"yes please"—

nausea overcome

habit forming

same as previous one if result pleasant (e.g. "made me feel grown-up"; "liked the feel of holding it"; "calmed my nerves")

3. repeated stimuli
"a packet of 20 please"

brain

same pathway used

automatic response
"I want a cigarette"—conditioned

20 Health Warning 20
20 Health Warning 20
20 Health Warning 20

4. no stimulus
body's metabolism now accustomed to drugs in cigarette and there are withdrawal symptoms if no cigarettes are available

same pathway

craved response—addicted
"I need a cigarette"

Summary/National Health Service

Main types of diseases

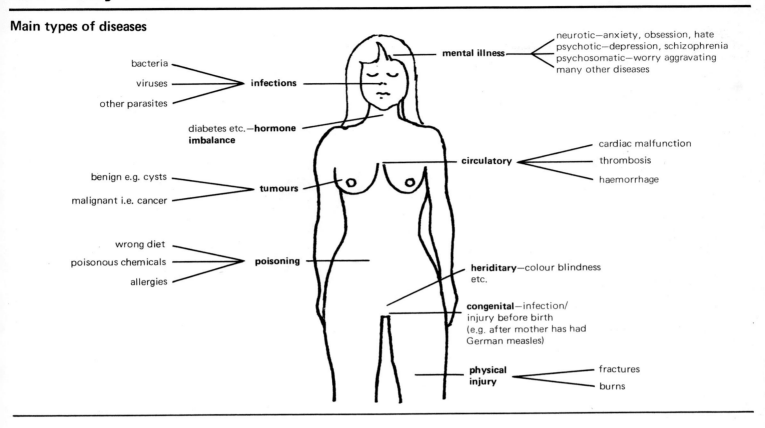

bacteria
viruses
other parasites
— **infections**

diabetes etc.—**hormone imbalance**

benign e.g. cysts
malignant i.e. cancer
— **tumours**

wrong diet
poisonous chemicals
allergies
— **poisoning**

mental illness
neurotic—anxiety, obsession, hate
psychotic—depression, schizophrenia
psychosomatic—worry aggravating
many other diseases

circulatory
cardiac malfunction
thrombosis
haemorrhage

heriditary—colour blindness etc.

congenital—infection/injury before birth (e.g. after mother has had German measles)

physical injury
fractures
burns

National Health Service

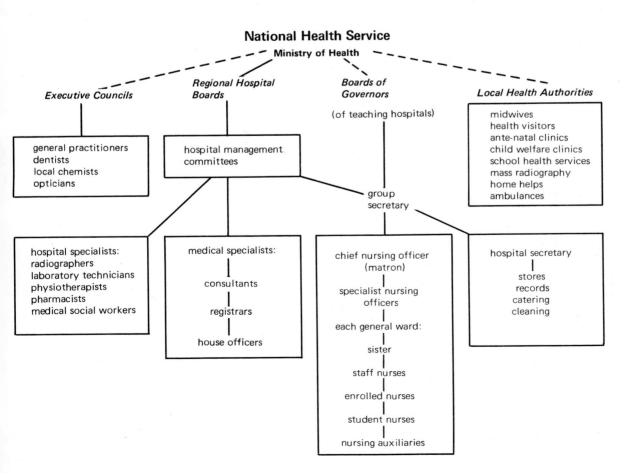

Ministry of Health

Executive Councils

Regional Hospital Boards

Boards of Governors
(of teaching hospitals)

Local Health Authorities

general practitioners
dentists
local chemists
opticians

hospital management committees

group secretary

midwives
health visitors
ante-natal clinics
child welfare clinics
school health services
mass radiography
home helps
ambulances

hospital specialists:
radiographers
laboratory technicians
physiotherapists
pharmacists
medical social workers

medical specialists:

consultants

registrars

house officers

chief nursing officer (matron)

specialist nursing officers

each general ward:

sister

staff nurses

enrolled nurses

student nurses

nursing auxiliaries

hospital secretary

stores
records
catering
cleaning

First aid

Procedure

If the reader has learned the structure and functioning of the human body, it should be easier to give correct first aid treatment in an emergency. The methods in this section have been simplified to help you remember them. Always bear in mind the anatomy of the injured organ. If possible, go to first aid classes and study a comprehensive manual. Practise methods as often as possible.

Basic rules

1. First-aid = first *aid*—it is only a temporary measure till expert help arrives.

2. The person is a casualty, not a patient—do not give "treatment", only give essential help.

3. You may have to give first aid in dangerous situations—always calculate the risk. Ignoring risks is stupid and may lead to another casualty—you!

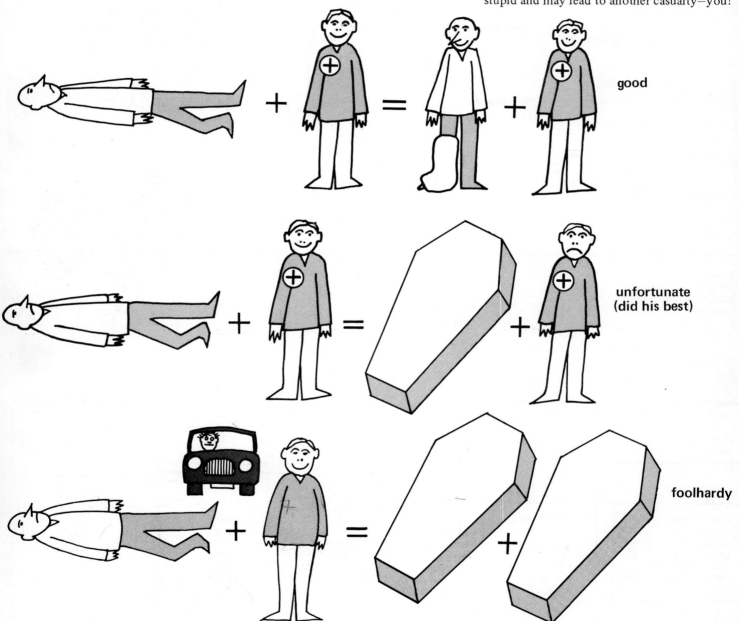

good

unfortunate
(did his best)

foolhardy

1 Survey the problem calmly	6 If in doubt, assume the worst—e.g. if unsure limb broken
2 Take care—ensure the safety of others and of self	
3 Ask others to summon help	7 Never try and remove a trapped, injured person unless absolutely necessary
4 Reassure the casualty	
5 Treat respiratory and cardiac failure urgently	8 Get as much practice of first aid techniques as possible

Discovering a serious accident

1. Is there any immediate danger? — other vehicles crashing
   — fire
   — exposed electric cables
   — falling building

Yes?—deal with the problem

No?—proceed to 2

2. Summon help:

   a Send two responsible persons in different directions to dial 999 and state:

   i position of accident
   ii number of casualties
   iii types of injury
   iv if fire brigade needed

   b Ask if anyone has experience of first aid—enlist their help,

   c If lot of casualties, show willing persons how to help

3. Look for casualties who will benefit from treatment:
   i leave the obviously dying
   ii leave the slightly injured

4. Quickly act to:

   i clear airways
   ii start breathing
   iii start heart
   iv control serious bleeding

5. Then:

   i examine casualty gently
   ii place in coma position if unconscious
   iii dress wounds with sterile dressings (or disposable tissues, clean sheets etc)
   iv immobilise any fractures
   v place in comfortable position and reassure
   vi look for signs of shock and treat

6. Do not:

   i give anything by mouth—this will make an emergency operation hazardous
   ii give hot water bottles or lots of blankets—the heat diverts blood away from vital organs, e.g. heart and brain, to skin

The coma position

Shock, fainting, epilepsy

Shock

This happens when the circulation of the blood is impeded so less blood flows to the brain and heart. The result may be more serious than the injury.

Common causes

1. Established shock—loss of blood

2. Nervous shock—result of unexpected event e.g. sudden noise, horrifying sight and to some extent with all injuries.

Signs — in order of appearance

A giddiness, feeling faint
B pale, cold, clammy skin
C nausea/vomiting
D shivering
E shallow, rapid breathing
F slow pulse
G rapid, feeble pulse
H unconsciousness

Treatment

As for prevention and:
i summon help—hospital treatment will probably be needed.
ii lay in coma position if unconscious.
iii cover with single blanket.

Prevented by:

1. Remove person to quiet place with fresh air. Reassure him.

2. Loosen tight clothing around neck, waist and chest.

3. Lay person on back with head to one side or sit with head between knees.

Fainting

Not enough blood gets to the brain

Common causes

Shock, fatigue, stuffy atmosphere

Signs

Like onset of shock

Treatment

As for prevention of shock

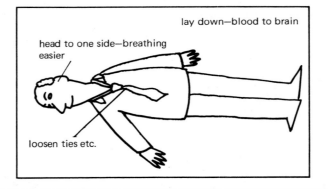

lay down—blood to brain

head to one side—breathing easier

loosen ties etc.

Epilepsy

Due to temporary malfunctioning of the brain causing temporary unconsciousness. There are two kinds:

Minor

A few seconds unconsciousness
B body stiffens
C eyes become glazed and staring
D soon resumes normal activity

Treatment —as for faint

Major

A falls to ground, face distorted, froths at mouth
B becomes rigid; spasms of muscles
C may bite tongue, lose control of bladder/bowels
D slowly recovers; becomes confused later

1. insert pencil or other hard object, preferably padded with a cloth or handkerchief between teeth (so tongue not bitten) but beware person does not bite through the object and choke. Guide movements of limbs so not injured.

2. do not leave person till his actions are back to normal

Bleeding/Particle in the eye

Minor wounds

1. Wash hands. Do not touch wound—skin covered with germs.
2. Clean area around wound with disinfectant.
3. Remove dirt and dead skin from wound by
   a   run under cold tap
   b   wipe in all directions away from wound with sterile gauze
   c   cover firmly with sterile dressing

antiseptic creams
iodine
germicide lotions

as these impede leucocytes
invading wound to eat
bacteria, dead skin etc.

Severe wounds

1. Lay person down with wound above body. Raise feet.

wound raised—

blood flows to brain more
easily

If no glass is present:

2. Press firmly on wound with sterile dressing for 10 minutes to allow clot to form.
3. Firmly bandage sterile dressing over whole area of wound.
4. Reassure casualty (he may lose two pints of blood with no serious consequences).
5. Beware of shock and treat if necessary.

Internal bleeding

1. Swelling of region—compare it with the other organ.
2. Pulse rate rises and increases whilst bleeding.
3. Sometimes blood passes through one of body's openings.

Treatment

As for severe wounds but do not bandage or press on injury—make casualty rest so clot forms naturally. If haemmorhage in chest, only recline person.

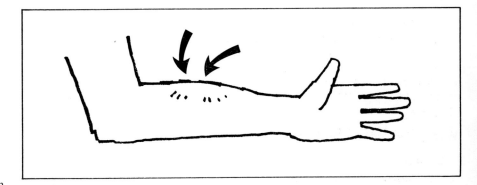

Black eye/bruising

Apply cold water or ice for several minutes—constricts sub-epidermal blood vessels so no more blood escapes.

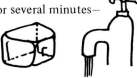

Particle in eye

1. Blink rapidly several times—tears may dislodge particles.
2. Get casualty to face light and look in all directions:
   a   particle not seen—pull upper lid over lower one and release
   b   particle seen—wash away with running water or moisten corner of clean handkerchief (or similar) and wipe off towards nose.
3. If particle stuck, cover eye and take to hospital.

Do not rub eye.

Nose bleeds

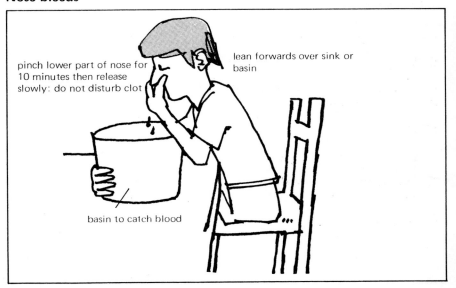

pinch lower part of nose for
10 minutes then release
slowly: do not disturb clot

lean forwards over sink or
basin

basin to catch blood

Fractures 1

Symptoms

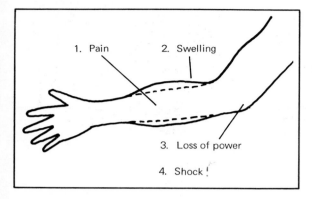

1. Pain
2. Swelling
3. Loss of power
4. Shock

Sometimes:
a mis-shapen bones
b bone penetrates skin (open, compound fractures)
c coughed-up blood (ribs fracture and penetrate lungs)
d depressed bone and some degree of unconsciousness (skull)

General treatment

1. Treat any wounds—
   see previous notes

2. Immobilise fracture so broken ends of bone don't cause further injury. Never twist the fractured organ.

3. Send casualty for X-ray and treatment. If in doubt, assume it is a fracture.

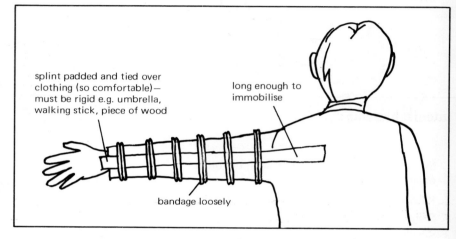

splint padded and tied over clothing (so comfortable)—must be rigid e.g. umbrella, walking stick, piece of wood

long enough to immobilise

bandage loosely

Ways of immobilising fractures

1. Skull:
   i Open fracture (bones pushed outwards)—bandage over wound firmly.
   ii Depressed fracture (bones pushed inwards)—bandage *around* but not over wound.

2. Jaw. Push lower jaw forwards and support with bandage from over head going underneath.

3 Vertebral column. Do not move person as broken bones may damage spinal cord causing paralysis.

4 Collar bone, arm, wrist. Fasten arm diagonally across chest so hand of damaged limb on opposite shoulder (cuff may be pinned to lapel of coat)

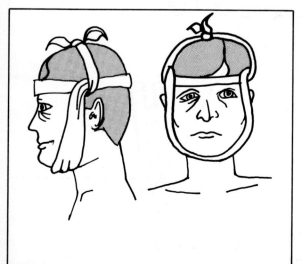

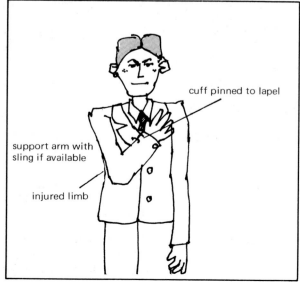

cuff pinned to lapel

support arm with sling if available

injured limb

Fractures 2

5. Ribs:

   a Blood coughed up (lung punctured)—lean person slightly *towards* damaged side so other lung can be used. Immobilise arm on injured side.

   b No blood—lean person *away* from injured side so ribs don't puncture lung. Bandage arm of injured side to side firmly.

6. Pelvis:

Lay down in most comfortable position— usually on back with knees slightly bent. Tie knees and ankles with soft padding between to prevent rotation of femur in acetabulum, if casualty to be transported.

tied together with padding between

firm surface   soft padding

7. Leg:

   a Thigh:

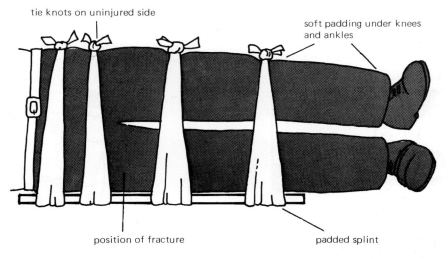

tie knots on uninjured side

soft padding under knees and ankles

lay casualty on his back

position of fracture   padded splint

note: do not tie over site of fracture—tie splint above and below injury

   b Below knee—as above but place splint between legs.

   c Ankle—lay on back, raise lower leg and support it on cushions (do not use splints)

   d Foot—leave shoe on to act as splint

Sprains

The ligaments at a joint are torn. Treat as for a fracture (it may be one).

Dislocations

Bones become displaced, usually at a hinge- or ball-and-socket joint. Causes unusual shape to limb. Treat as for fracture.

Burns/Scalds/Electric shocks

Burns/scalds

1. Loss of plasma
   - swelling ----- Remove rings etc. at once
   - dehydration ---- Give frequent sips of water/tea

2. Pain (damaged skin receptors) ------- Run under cold tap for few minutes

3. Allow bacteria to enter
   - Cover with sterile dressing
   - Do not remove burnt clothing (bandage on top)
   - Do not burst blisters

4. Scarring if larger than 1p piece ----- Hospitalise as skin graft may be needed

5. Shock if major burn --------- See other notes

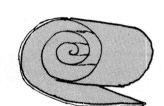

Chemical burns

A Wash off chemical immediately with lots of water
B Remove contaminated clothing
C Treat as for heat burn

Electric shock

1. Switch off electricity before touching casualty, else electricity may pass through you. If possible
   - a stand on dry, non-metallic substance and remove person
   - b wear rubber gloves to remove him

2. Start artificial respiration/cardiac massage

3. Treat any burns as above

4. Treat for shock

electricity may cause heart and respiratory failure

path of electricity

electricity cannot pass

Poisoning

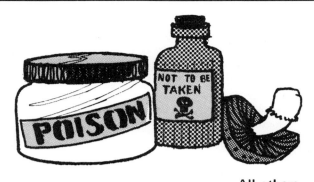

1. Ask person what happened
2. Call medical help
3. Keep some of unswallowed poison or vomit
4. Look for signs and act:

	Corrosive poisons concentrated acids, alkalis, phenol etc.	**All others** tablets, lead paint, fungi, rat poison, insecticides, plants etc.
Symptoms	lips, mouth and throat burned; great pain; shock	usually nausea, lethargy or other abnormal behaviour
Action	1. Acids swallowed—give alkali e.g. Milk of Magnesia or other substance for indigestion 2. Alkali (e.g. ammonia)—give acid e.g. vinegar, pure lemon juice 3. Phenol (in some disinfectants)—give laxative + lot of water only	For all of the above call for medical help immediately, then if you have time: 1. Make him vomit ← 2 tablespoons salt in water / 2 tablespoons mustard in water / Fingers thrust down throat 2. Give lots of water/tea/milk/coffee 3. Give strong laxative—not liquid paraffin as may be vomited up and inspired causing suffocation. 4. Keep casualty still.

Then

Keep under close observation. If ← unconscious—lay in coma position / breathing stops—artificial respiration / heart stops—cardiac massage.

Never
1. Give antidote for corrosive poison if poison swallowed not known.
2. Give person who has swallowed a corrosive poison a substance to make him vomit.
3. Give children full dose of antidote, laxative etc.:

Age	Amount
8–14	¾ dose
2–8	½ dose
1–2	¼ dose
under 1	1/8 dose

Exposure/Heart attack

Exposure

Due to blood cooling too much. Greater chance of this if skin wet as water evaporates like sweat (see notes on temperature control of blood). All body's metabolism slows down—usual signs are:

1. Person becomes dreamy and apathetic—brain affected as the most sensitive organ.

2. Drunken walk—muscles weaken.

3. Tiredness leading to unconsciousness.

4. Death.

Treatment

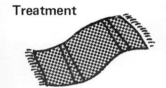

a dry the skin remove wet clothes   *b* put on warm, dry clothing   *c* shelter from wind   *d* hotdrinks + hot bath if available

Heart attack

Due to inadequate blood supply to cardiac muscle—coronary arteries narrow due to spasm (angina pectoris) or clot forms in arteries (coronary thrombosis). Signs:

in region of heart—spreads to shoulders and arms

breathlessness

irregular, weak pulse

shock

angina pectoris—person soon recovers

coronary thrombosis—slow recovery, needs hospital treatment

Treatment

rest person in comfortable position. Loosen tight clothing

be prepared to give cardiac massage and artificial respiration

dial 999 for ambulance

Drowning

Drowning

Water enters bronchioles and prevents gaseous exchange. Carbon dioxide increases in blood, oxygen decreases causing paralysis of respiratory muscles and heart.

Artificial respiration must begin as soon as possible.

1. Retrieve body—a drowned person usually sinks.

2. Clear mouth and throat of any foreign bodies at once.

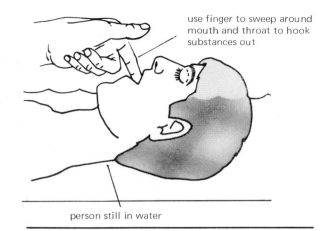

use finger to sweep around mouth and throat to hook substances out

person still in water

3. Whilst person still in water, start mouth-to-nose or mouth-to-mouth respiration.

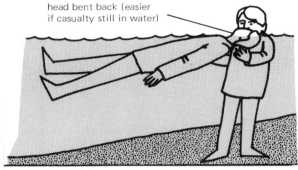

head bent back (easier if casualty still in water)

4. Bring casualty to shore and continue respiration for at least one hour or until he can breath properly by himself.

5. Periodically check pulse—if heart stops, apply cardiac massage.

6. Lay in coma position with head downwards (to let water drain away).

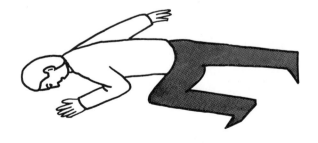

Gassing

Results—similar to drowning
Treatment—remove to fresh air, then artificial respiration and coma position

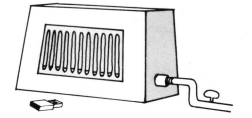

Artificial respiration

This must be started as soon as possible because the brain begins to deteriorate irrevocably after five minutes without oxygen.

Before starting

1. Remove false teeth, vomit and any other objects blocking mouth and throat—use finger to hook debris out. Hold head back so tongue doesn't block pharynx.

2. Make sure person cannot breath by himself—if breathing feeble, treat as if not breathing. Lay in coma position if he is breathing.

3. Apply artificial respiration once every 4-5 seconds.

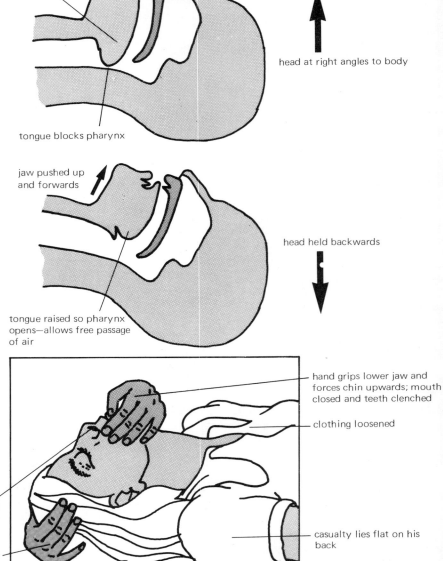

lower jaw and tongue fallen back

head at right angles to body

tongue blocks pharynx

jaw pushed up and forwards

head held backwards

tongue raised so pharynx opens—allows free passage of air

The head must therefore be held back with hand under lower jaw to support it if artificial respiration given to casualty lying on his back.

Mouth-to-nose method

Preferred to the mouth-to-mouth method as less chance of blowing into the stomach which may stimulate it to vomit (and the vomit may be inspired). Also the mouth must be closed so there is less chance of the tongue blocking the pharynx.

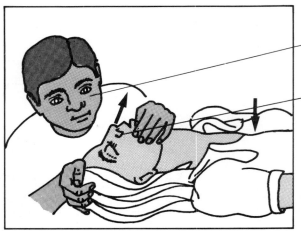

hand grips lower jaw and forces chin upwards; mouth closed and teeth clenched

clothing loosened

first-aider seals his lips here and blows

hand forces head backwards

casualty lies flat on his back

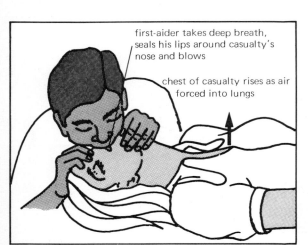

first-aider takes deep breath, seals his lips around casualty's nose and blows

chest of casualty rises as air forced into lungs

first-aider stops blowing and watches casualty's chest fall

air expired

whole process repeated every 4-5 seconds

Artificial respiration

Silvester's method

This method, like the mouth-to-nose method, allows external cardiac massage to be applied by another helper at the same time. It can be used when the face is injured.

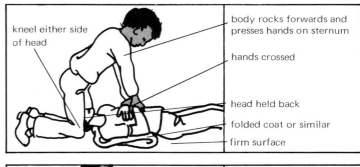

kneel either side of head

body rocks forwards and presses hands on sternum

hands crossed

head held back

folded coat or similar

firm surface

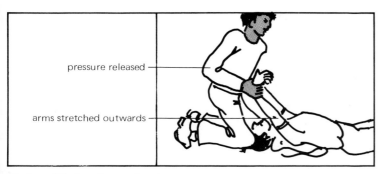

pressure released

arms stretched outwards

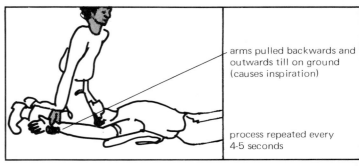

arms pulled backwards and outwards till on ground (causes inspiration)

process repeated every 4-5 seconds

Holger-Nielsen's method

This method allows water to drain out of the lungs but does not permit cardiac massage to be applied at the same time.

If there is no inspiration, thump the casualty between the shoulder blades to remove any obstruction; for children, hold upside-down by feet and slap on back.

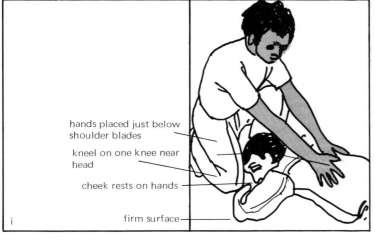

hands placed just below shoulder blades

kneel on one knee near head

cheek rests on hands

firm surface

i

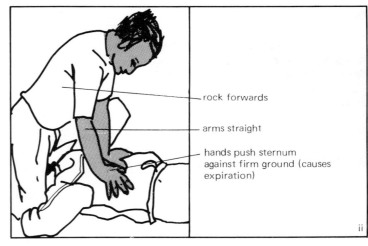

rock forwards

arms straight

hands push sternum against firm ground (causes expiration)

ii

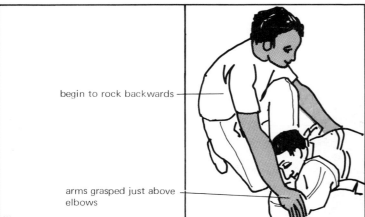

begin to rock backwards

arms grasped just above elbows

iii

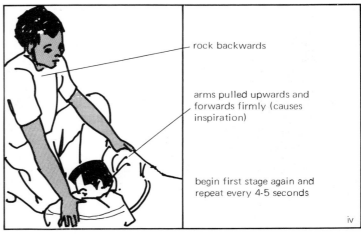

rock backwards

arms pulled upwards and forwards firmly (causes inspiration)

begin first stage again and repeat every 4-5 seconds

iv

Artificial respiration

External cardiac massage

Make sure the heart has stopped before starting to massage. Signs are:

1. No pulse

2. Pupils widely dilated

3. Skin has waxy-blue-grey colour

If the heart has stopped, place person on hard surface and:

1. Strike here smartly once

This may stimulate the heart to start beating. Feel for pulse, look at pupils (will contract if heart starts)

2. If still not started, begin external massage.

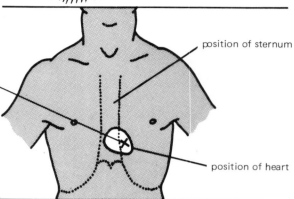

pupils widely dilated-
muscles of iris fully
relaxed, even in bright light

position of sternum

position of heart

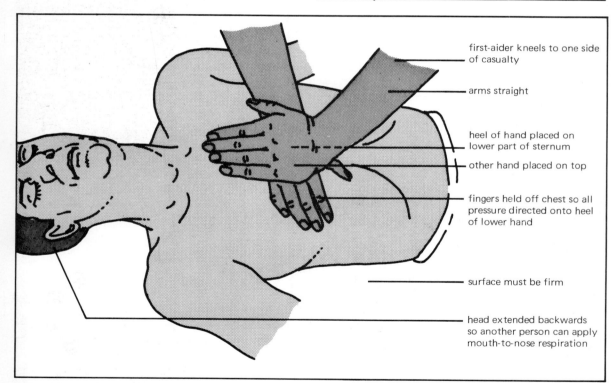

first-aider kneels to one side
of casualty

arms straight

heel of hand placed on
lower part of sternum

other hand placed on top

fingers held off chest so all
pressure directed onto heel
of lower hand

surface must be firm

head extended backwards
so another person can apply
mouth-to-nose respiration

Press firmly once every second, continue till casualty reaches hospital

For children—pressure of one hand enough

For babies—pressure of two fingers only

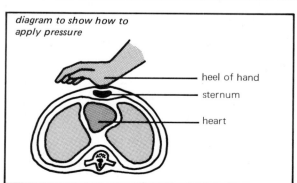

diagram to show how to
apply pressure

heel of hand

sternum

heart

Medical machines
The artificial kidney

The kidney machine

One function of the kidney is to remove from the blood the waste product of protein metabolism urea.

When for one reason or another, the kidneys are not performing their functions adequately, the artificial kidney may be employed.

machine which produces solution of mineral salts at the correct concentration and temperature

Actual kidney through which blood passes

Photo provided by Lucas Med. Equip.

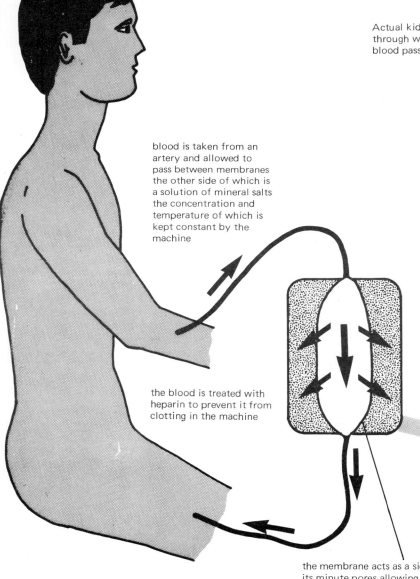

blood is taken from an artery and allowed to pass between membranes the other side of which is a solution of mineral salts the concentration and temperature of which is kept constant by the machine

the blood is treated with heparin to prevent it from clotting in the machine

the membrane acts as a sieve, its minute pores allowing the small molecules of urea to diffuse across from the blood into the mineral salt solution but preventing other components with larger particles for example proteins, from leaving the blood

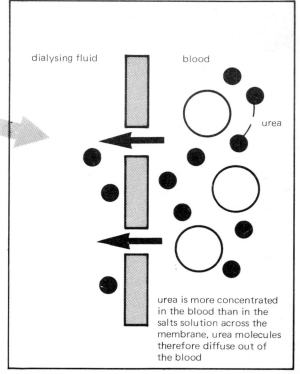

dialysing fluid   blood

urea

urea is more concentrated in the blood than in the salts solution across the membrane, urea molecules therefore diffuse out of the blood

The respirator

Iron lung

This machine takes over the job of the breathing muscles when they are paralysed by disease for example in poliomyelitis.

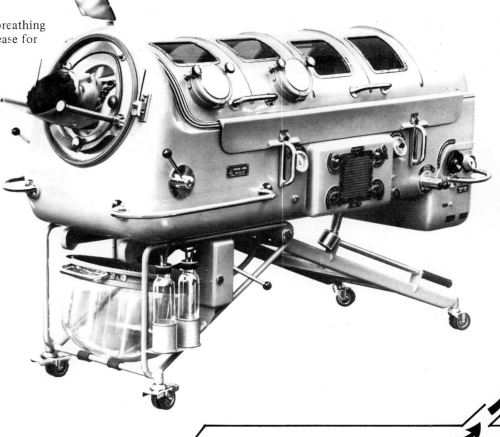

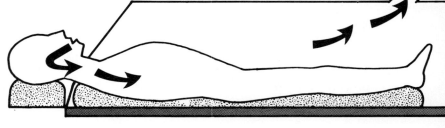

1 air is sucked out so that the pressure around the patient's chest is reduced. The patient's chest expands and air is sucked into the lungs

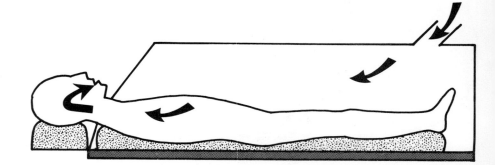

2 air is returned so that pressure is again normal. The patient's chest wall contracts and air is forced out of the lungs

In another type of respirator, a tube is inserted into the patient's trachea and air is forced through this tube to inflate the lungs.

This type of machine is often used during operations when the surgeon has given a drug to paralyse the breathing muscles.

The heart-lung machine

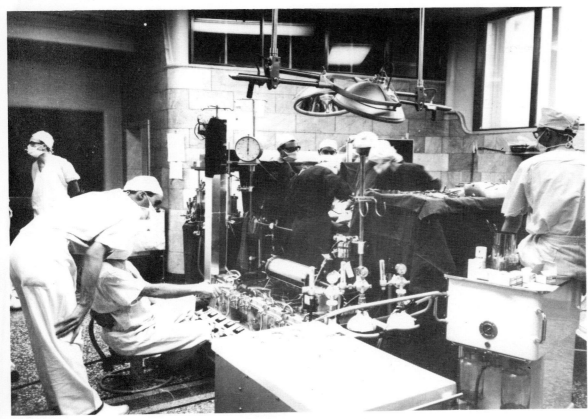

The heart-lung machine carries out the job of the heart and lungs enabling surgeons to perform operations on the heart often lasting many hours.

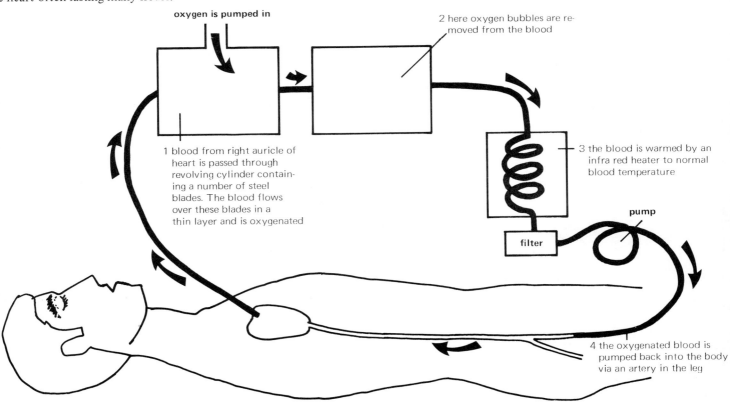

oxygen is pumped in

2 here oxygen bubbles are removed from the blood

1 blood from right auricle of heart is passed through revolving cylinder containing a number of steel blades. The blood flows over these blades in a thin layer and is oxygenated

3 the blood is warmed by an infra red heater to normal blood temperature

pump

filter

4 the oxygenated blood is pumped back into the body via an artery in the leg

The X-Ray apparatus

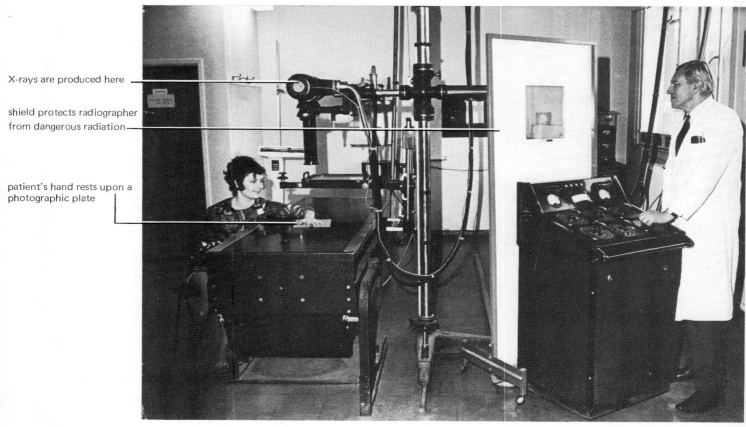

X-rays are produced here

shield protects radiographer
from dangerous radiation

patient's hand rests upon a
photographic plate

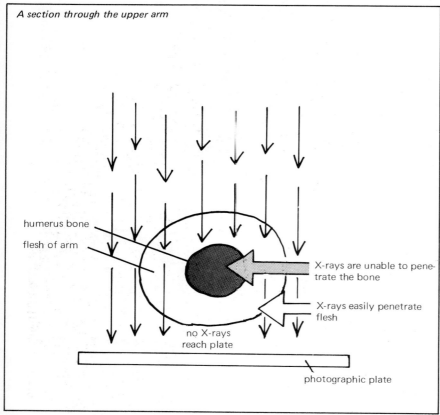

A section through the upper arm

humerus bone

flesh of arm

X-rays are unable to penetrate the bone

X-rays easily penetrate
flesh

no X-rays
reach plate

photographic plate

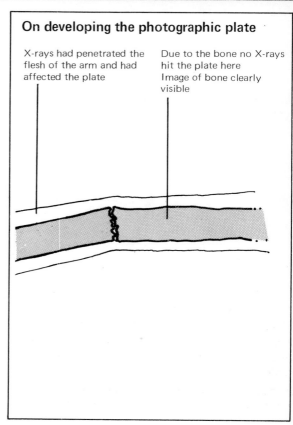

On developing the photographic plate

X-rays had penetrated the
flesh of the arm and had
affected the plate

Due to the bone no X-rays
hit the plate here
Image of bone clearly
visible

The electrocardiogram E.C.G.

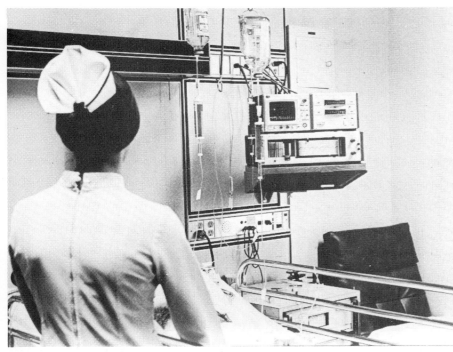

The electrocardiogram E.C.G.
This type of machine is used in hospitals.

The recording apparatus is mounted on the wall at the patient's bedside.

This type of machine is portable and can be taken to a patient's home by a G.P.

trace showing electrical activity during the beating of the heart

During the beating of the heart, small electric currents or impulses as they are called, pass across the heart.

In the electrocardiogram, electrodes attached to the patient's body pick up these impulses, they are amplified and recorded.

By studying an electrocardiograph much can be learned about the way in which the heart is functioning.

Practical work

Using a microscope

Innumerable experiments can be performed which are related to Human Biology. A selection has been made to indicate the most important skills a science student should acquire. The skills are:

Some modern microscopes have built-in lamps so they have no mirror or condenser to adjust.

Most microscopes are par-focal i.e. if the lower power objective is focused (using the coarse adjustment), the high power objective will also be in focus if rotated to come under the eyepiece. Only minor adjustments using the fine adjustment knob will be necessary.

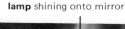

lamp shining onto mirror

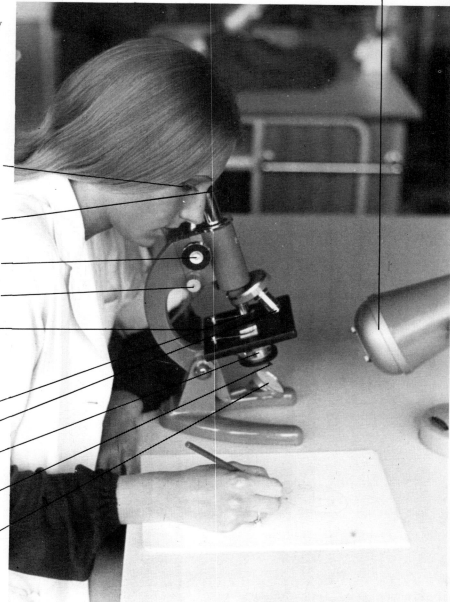

left eye looks down microscope so right eye can look at drawing (opposite if left-handed)

eyepiece of microscope clean

coarse adjustment

fine adjustment

stage—can be slanted if slide is a permanent one (not if it has a temporary drop of water only)

low power objective lens

high power objective lens

condenser adjusted to give even light—best position usually near stage

diaphragm lever—adjusts light intensity

mirror adjusted to reflect light up through condenser and slide

Making microscope slides

V. S. Prepared permanent slide

mountant—"glue" to prevent moisture getting to specimen; also sticks cover slip in place

cover slip—thin piece of glass

microscope slide—glass

specimen—thin smear or section (must be thin to allow light to pass through it) dehydrated (so bacteria etc. cannot feed on it)

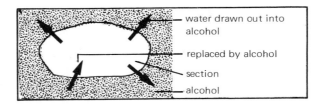

In order to dehydrate sections, they are placed in various concentrations of alcohol. The strength of alcohol around the section is gradually increased till it is absolute (100%). All the water is then removed after approximately one minute.

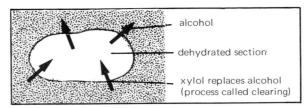

water drawn out into alcohol

replaced by alcohol

section

alcohol

The mountant (e.g. Canada Balsam) is a resin dissolved in xylol, not alcohol. The alcohol must therefore be replaced by xylol after the section has been dehydrated:-

alcohol

dehydrated section

xylol replaces alcohol (process called clearing)

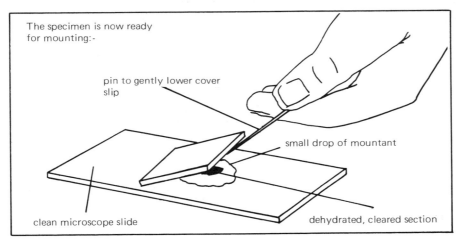

The specimen is now ready for mounting:-

pin to gently lower cover slip

small drop of mountant

clean microscope slide

dehydrated, cleared section

Staining

If the section or smear is transparent, it must be stained before it can be seen using an ordinary light microscope. Stains used are dissolved in alcohol so that the specimen can be stained whilst dehydrating. A typical staining schedule is:-

1 70% alcohol
2 Borax Carmine stain (in 70% alcohol)
3 70% alcohol (to remove excess stain)
4 90% alcohol
5 100% alcohol ⎤
6 100% alcohol ⎥ two changes of each to ensure all the alcohol/xylol removed
7 xylol ⎥
8 xylol ⎦
9 mount
10 allow several days to dry

N. B. each stage is approximately one minute

Smears
These are prepared as follows:-

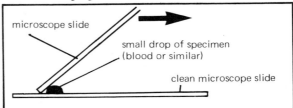

microscope slide

small drop of specimen (blood or similar)

clean microscope slide

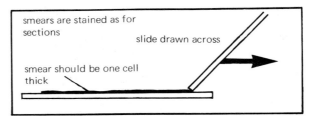

smears are stained as for sections

slide drawn across

smear should be one cell thick

If no permanent slide is required, the smear/section can be stained and mounted in water or glycerin. No dehydrating or clearing is necessary.

Drawings/Recordings

These should be as accurate and clear as possible. All mistakes must be corrected.

Drawings

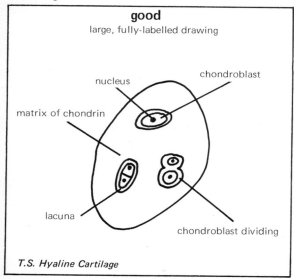

good

large, fully-labelled drawing

nucleus

chondroblast

matrix of chondrin

lacuna

chondroblast dividing

T.S. Hyaline Cartilage

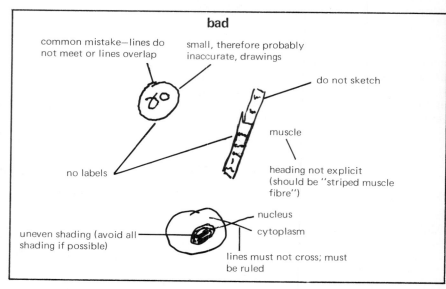

bad

common mistake—lines do not meet or lines overlap

small, therefore probably inaccurate, drawings

do not sketch

muscle

heading not explicit (should be "striped muscle fibre")

no labels

uneven shading (avoid all shading if possible)

nucleus

cytoplasm

lines must not cross; must be ruled

N.B.

   T.S. = transverse section
   V.S. = vertical section
   L.S. = longitudinal section

1. a sharp pencil about 1H is best
2. rub out any mistakes neatly
3. use a ruler for guide lines
4. use drawing, not lined, paper

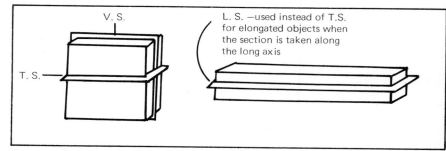

V. S.

T. S.

L. S. —used instead of T.S. for elongated objects when the section is taken along the long axis

Recordings

a Readings of the levels of liquids are taken to the bottom of the meniscus:-

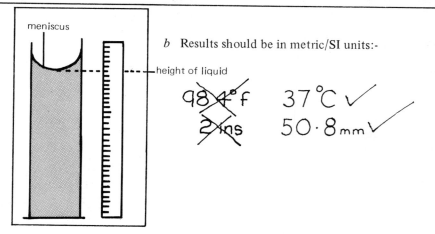

meniscus

height of liquid

b Results should be in metric/SI units:-

98·4°f ✗   37°C ✓

2ins ✗   50·8mm ✓

c Record data/figures in tables if possible. Units of measurement must be shown:-

Temperature (°C)	Time (seconds)
10	124
15	80
20	72
25	63
30	61

units recorded at top of table, not after each reading

An experiment to demonstrate the principles of digestion

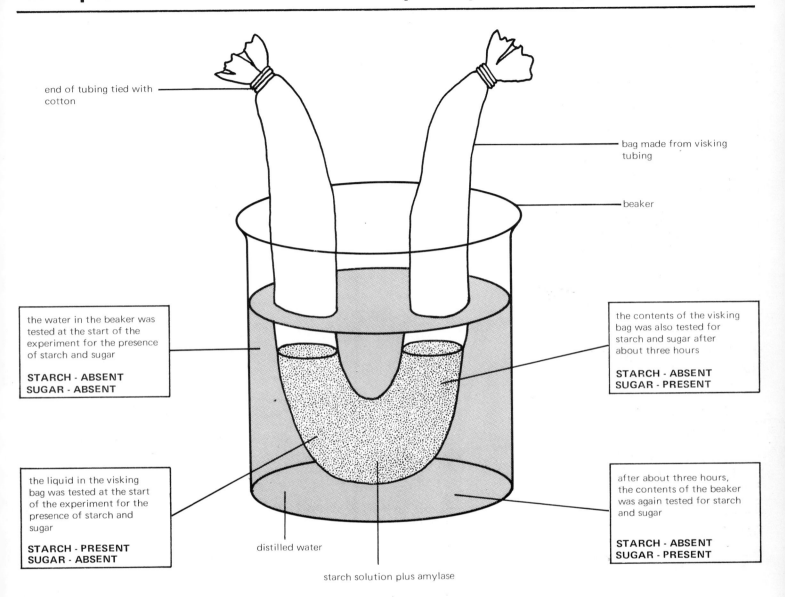

end of tubing tied with cotton

bag made from visking tubing

beaker

the water in the beaker was tested at the start of the experiment for the presence of starch and sugar

STARCH - ABSENT
SUGAR - ABSENT

the contents of the visking bag was also tested for starch and sugar after about three hours

STARCH - ABSENT
SUGAR - PRESENT

the liquid in the visking bag was tested at the start of the experiment for the presence of starch and sugar

STARCH - PRESENT
SUGAR - ABSENT

after about three hours, the contents of the beaker was again tested for starch and sugar

STARCH - ABSENT
SUGAR - PRESENT

distilled water

starch solution plus amylase

From this experiment it can be concluded that starch does not pass across the wall of the visking sac. The starch molecules are too big to pass through the minute pores. However in the presence of amylase, the starch molecules are hydrolysed to form much smaller molecules of maltose sugar. The presence of sugar in the contents of the beaker at the end of the experiment show that these molecules do diffuse across the wall of the visking sac.

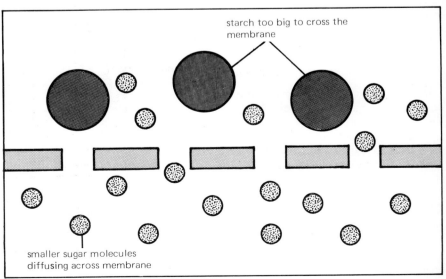

starch too big to cross the membrane

smaller sugar molecules diffusing across membrane

An investigation into lung capacities

(i) Tidal volume   (ii) Complementary air   (iii) Supplementary air

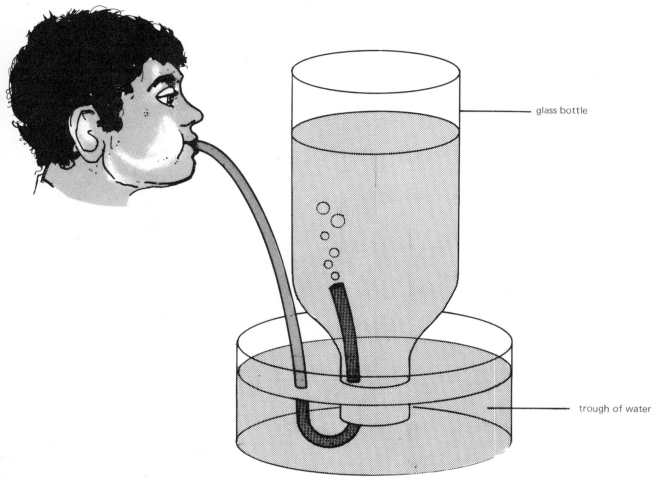

glass bottle

trough of water

(1) To measure the tidal volume

Take a normal breath in, place tube in mouth and breathe out as if breathing normally. Measure the volume of water displaced which will be the volume of air expired.

(2) To measure complementary air

The bottle should contain only a little water of known volume and the rubber tube should be above the level of the water in the bottle. Breathe in normally, place tube in mouth and then breathe in as much as possible; water will enter the bottle. Measure the volume to find the volume of complementary air

(3) To measure supplementary air

Set up the apparatus as in the diagram, breathe out normally, then blow as hard and for as long as possible, the volume of water displaced will be the volume of supplementary air.

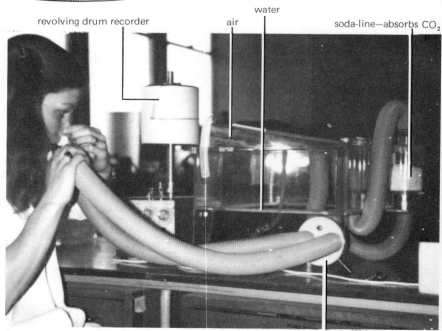

revolving drum recorder   air   water   soda-line—absorbs CO_2

Recording Spirometer   inlet and outlet valves

138

An experiment to investigate the bacteria in the air

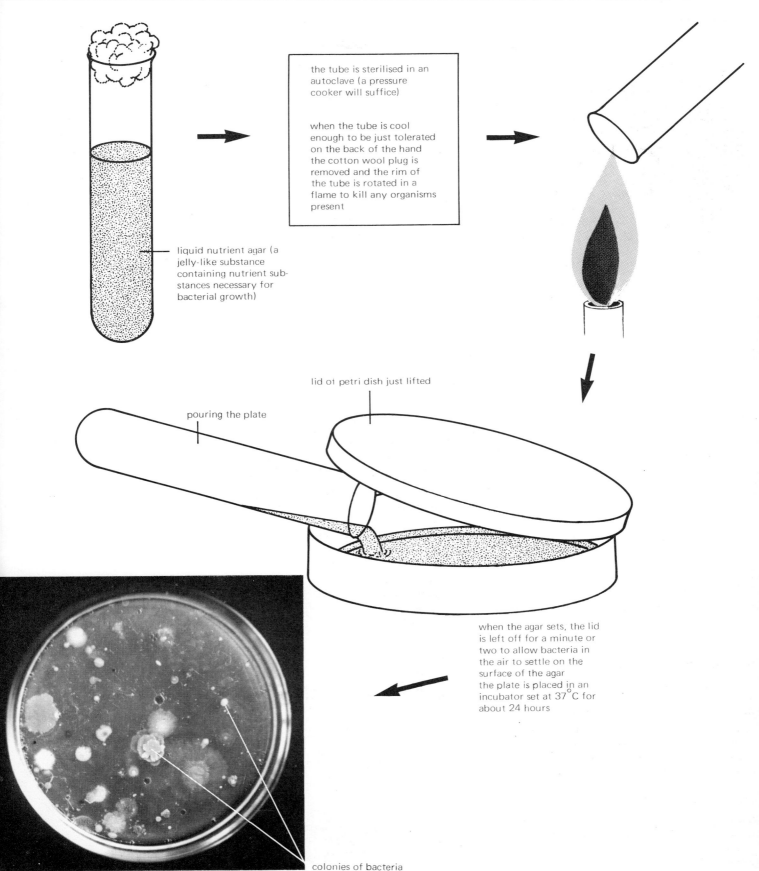

liquid nutrient agar (a jelly-like substance containing nutrient substances necessary for bacterial growth)

the tube is sterilised in an autoclave (a pressure cooker will suffice)

when the tube is cool enough to be just tolerated on the back of the hand the cotton wool plug is removed and the rim of the tube is rotated in a flame to kill any organisms present

lid of petri dish just lifted

pouring the plate

when the agar sets, the lid is left off for a minute or two to allow bacteria in the air to settle on the surface of the agar
the plate is placed in an incubator set at 37°C for about 24 hours

colonies of bacteria

Experimenting with human senses

Individual results of experiments on people vary a lot. The variations are due to differences in the sensitivity of sense organs of different people. Many results must be obtained from several people and the results averaged before they can be relied on as being "typical". Below is an example of such an experiment.

An experiment on touch receptors

1. Touch the palm of the subject's hand with one point, then two points wide apart (over 10 mm) so that the subject knows the stimuli to expect.
2. With the points in line with the middle finger, determine the minimum distance between points that the subject can detect two pricks and not one. This is done by:-
a Repeatedly touch the centre of the palm with two points and ask if he feels one point or two. Record all results.
b Occasionally touch the palm with one point only to see if he is cheating.
c Gradually lessen the distance between the points until the subject can only feel one prick when two points are applied.
d Slightly widen the points till the subject feels two pricks about 75% of the time. The distance between the points is recond as the average separation between different touch receptors.
3. Repeat 1. and 2. using the pins/dividers at right angles to the points above. Are there any differences between these results and those in 2? If so, why?
4. Repeat 1 — 3 on different parts of the palm, fingers, back of the hand, forearm etc. to discover any differences in distribution of touch receptors.
5. Repeat 1 — 4 on many subjects and average the results (or take the results of a class and average them). Only these results can be taken as typical.

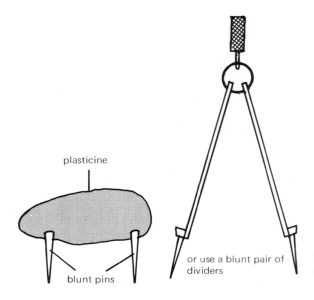

plasticine

blunt pins

or use a blunt pair of dividers

The experiment is performed on a blindfolded subject

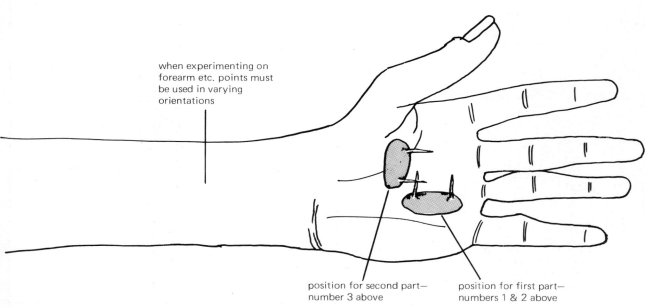

when experimenting on forearm etc. points must be used in varying orientations

position for second part— number 3 above

position for first part— numbers 1 & 2 above

Some simple biochemical tests on food

A test for starch

a small piece of the food is placed in a tube and covered with water. The tube is then heated

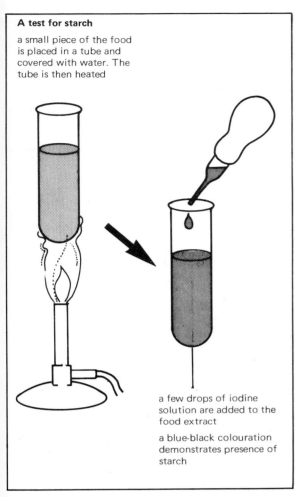

a few drops of iodine solution are added to the food extract

a blue-black colouration demonstrates presence of starch

A test for a sugar
(reducing sugar)

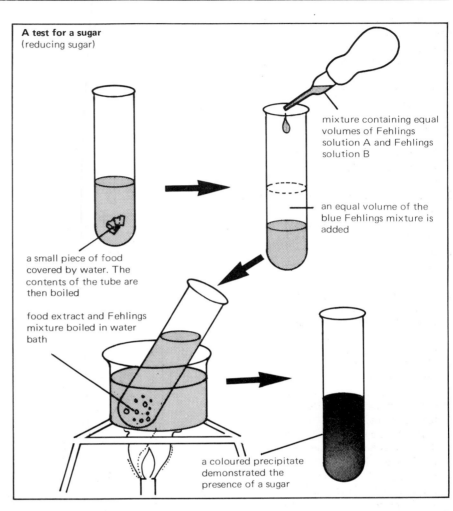

a small piece of food covered by water. The contents of the tube are then boiled

mixture containing equal volumes of Fehlings solution A and Fehlings solution B

an equal volume of the blue Fehlings mixture is added

food extract and Fehlings mixture boiled in water bath

a coloured precipitate demonstrated the presence of a sugar

A test for a fat

filter paper

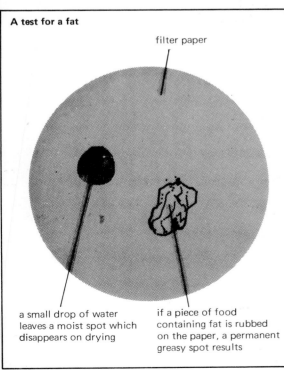

a small drop of water leaves a moist spot which disappears on drying

if a piece of food containing fat is rubbed on the paper, a permanent greasy spot results

A test for protein

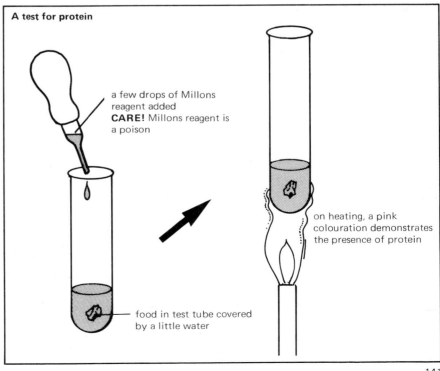

a few drops of Millons reagent added
CARE! Millons reagent is a poison

on heating, a pink colouration demonstrates the presence of protein

food in test tube covered by a little water

Questions

Tables

This section gives the student some idea of the types of questions asked in examination. Some hints are given underneath each type to indicate how they should be answered.

Completion of a table

Complete the following table in the spaces provided to indicate the endocrine gland, its location, a hormone it secretes and the main effect of the hormone.

GLAND	LOCATION	HORMONE	MAIN EFFECT
Islets of Langerhans	in pancreas	insulin	stimulates liver to convert blood glucose to glycogen
	in scrotal sacs		
thyroid			
		adrenaline	
			promotes development of lining of uterus
		prolactin	

Notes

Be as specific as possible e.g. adrenaline is secreted by the adrenal medulla, not just the adrenal.

Most hormones have alternative names which are acceptable in answers e.g. adrenaline = epinephrine. Alternative names can be given in a table so students should be aware of other names.

Answers must be concise in order to fit into the spaces provided e.g. the main effects of hormones in the above table.

Copy the following paragraph into your book, filling in the gaps:

The . . . . is the bone of the upper arm and its upper portion has a rounded end called the . . . . which articulates with the . . . . cavity of the . . . . girdle. At its lower end it articulates with the . . . . and the . . . . and the largest muscle, called the . . . . which flexes these bones against the upper arm is inserted on the . . . . The main extensor muscle antagonistic to the above muscle is the . . . .

Notes

This type of question is very similar to a table and also requires short, usually one-word answers. Make sure the first parts are answered correctly as subsequent answers usually depend on these. (Some students may assume that the question is concerned with the femur and leg and will therefore get all the answers wrong.)

Answers

humerus, head, glenoid, pectoral, radius, ulna, brachialis, ulna, triceps.

Drawing graphs

Some human blood was exposed to oxygen so that the amount of haemoglobin saturated with oxygen (expressed as a percentage) could be found. Different concentrations (partial pressures in mm mercury) of oxygen were used to determine their effect on the percentage saturation. Below are the results of the experiment.

oxygen concentration mm mercury	% saturation haemoglobin
12	10
21	30
40	68
65	87
90	95

a. Draw a graph of the results.

b. Using the graph determine the percentage saturation of haemoglobin at 30 mm oxygen . . . . .

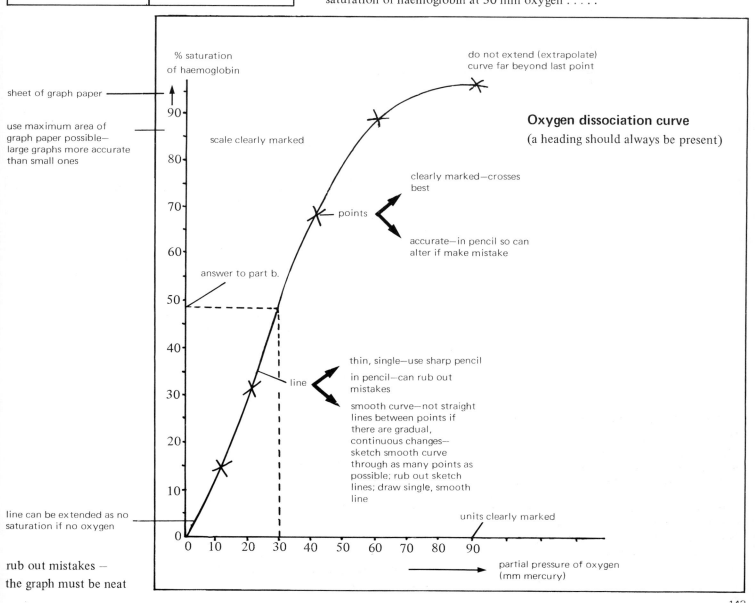

Analysing the results of an experiment

The diagram below shows the apparatus used in an experiment to demonstrate the action of salivary amylase (ptyalin)

Three tests for the presence of starch (iodine test) and reducing sugar (Fehlings test) were carried out at five minute intervals on the solutions inside the visking tubing and outside in the beaker. Some diluted saliva was then added to the contents of the visking tubing, and the tests were repeated at five-minute intervals. The table below shows the results of the experiment.

(a) Account for the results

(b) Describe any modifications which you could make to this experiment to learn more about salivary amylase

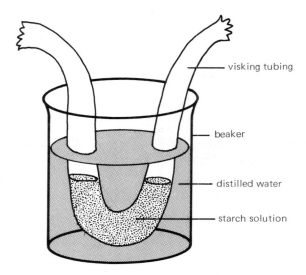

visking tubing

beaker

distilled water

starch solution

		minutes before the addition of saliva			minutes after the addition of saliva		
		15	10	5	5	10	15
inside visking tubing	starch	✓	✓	✓	✓	✓	✓
	sugar	✗	✗	✗	✓	✓	✓
outside visking tubing	starch	✗	✗	✗	✗	✗	✗
	sugar	✗	✗	✗	✗	✓	✓

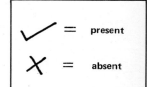

✓ = present

✗ = absent

Answer

a From the table it can be seen that at the start of the experiment before the addition of saliva, starch was present only inside the visking tubing. There was no sugar either inside or outside the visking tubing. Five minutes after the addition of saliva to the contents of the tubing sugar was present within the visking tubing. This was due to the fact that in the presence of the enzyme salivary amylase, the starch was hydrolysed to form the sugar maltose. Ten minutes after the addition of saliva, sugar was also detected in the liquid outside the visking tubing. This was due to the fact that the sugar molecules had diffused through the visking membrane. There was no starch detected outside the visking tubing fifteen minutes after the addition of the saliva. This was because the starch molecules being very big, were unable to pass through the minute pores in the membrane.

b There are several ways in which this experiment could be modified to enable one to learn more about this enzyme, for example.

i The experiment could be performed several times, the water in the beaker being kept at a different temperature for each experiment. This would enable one to demonstrate the effect of temperature on amylase activity.

ii By means of buffers, the pH of solution could be varied.

iii The saliva could first be boiled to demonstrate the effect of subjecting an enzyme to heat.

A question of the labelling of a diagram

The diagram shows a section through the skin

1. label the parts a - h
2. state how the blood capillaries labelled X in the diagram are concerned in temperature regulation.

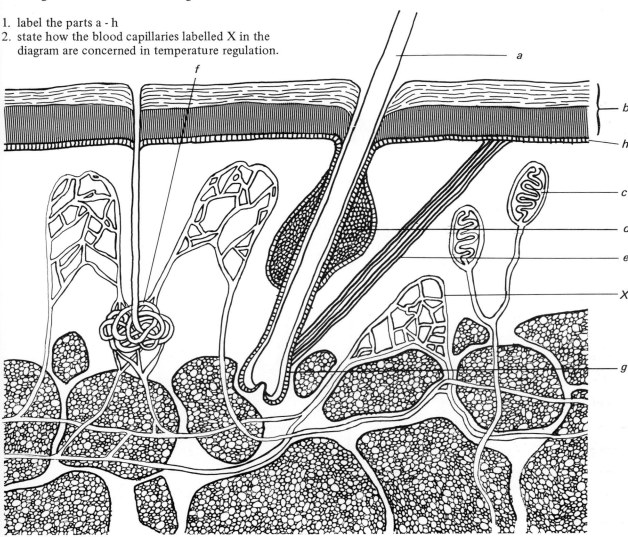

Answer

a Hair   *b* Epidermis   *c* Nerve ending

d Sebaceous gland   *e* Erector muscle

f Sweat gland   *g* Hair follicle   *h* Malpighian layer

2 When the body is overheated, the tiny capillaries in the skin dilate (open up) allowing more blood to flow close to the surface of the body so that more heat is lost. When the body is cold, the capillaries constrict, so that less blood flows close to the body surface and less heat is lost.

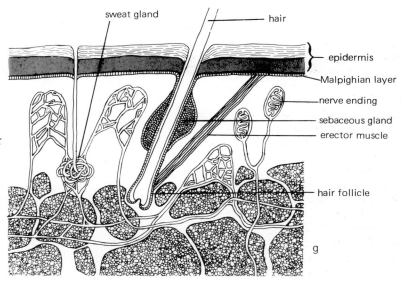

Interpreting a photograph

A On the photographs below label one thing that could possibly:

a aggravate a person suffering from bronchitis

b cause a fracture of the femur

c be a source of *Salmonella* bacteria.

Note: The question goes on to ask you to use arrows labelled *a, b* and *c*; the points of the arrows are to be exactly on the object.

B State why you consider each a possible hazard to health.

Examination papers can contain photographs of any part of the human body or a photograph of a situation relevant to the subjects in a syllabus. Students should be aware of the actual structure of organs, tissues etc. and should study situations/areas to see if any health hazards are present.

Analysing an experiment

An investigation into the concentration of various substances in urine and plasma was carried out, the results appearing in the table below.

substance	plasma %	urine %
water	90.93	95.00
proteins	7.90	0.00
urea	0.03	2.00
mineral ions	0.71	0.46
glucose	0.10	0.00

a Name the substances which are absent from the urine but which are present in the blood plasma

b Explain these results

Answers

a Proteins and glucose are absent from urine but present in the plasma.

b In the Bowman's capsule, the relatively small particles of water, glucose, urea and mineral salts are forced under pressure from the blood into the kidney tubule. Protein molecules being very big remain in the blood, hence their absence from the urine. As the filtrate passes around the tubule all the glucose and some of the salts are reabsorbed into the blood. Hence the absence of glucose in urine and lower concentration of mineral ions.

The table below shows the concentration of protein, chloride, calcium and urea in blood plasma and in tissue fluid.

substance	plasma	tissue fluid
protein (g/100ml)	6.90	0.10
chloride (m.equiv./l)	100.00	104.00
calcium (m.equiv./l)	5.20	5.00
urea (mh/100ml)	22.00	22.00

a What can be said about the differences in concentration of the four constituents in plasma and tissue fluid?

b Using your knowledge of tissue fluid formation, explain the data.

Answer

a The concentration of protein is much higher in the plasma than tissue fluid, only a small amount of protein in the latter.

The concentrations of chloride, calcium and urea are similar in both plasma and tissue fluid.

b Blood at the arterial end of a capillary is under greater pressure than at the venous end. Water, together with substances of small molecular weight, is forced out through the capillary wall to bathe the tissues. Protein molecules are large and are not therefore forced out and remain in the blood. The molecules of calcium, chloride and urea are smaller and pass through the capillary wall and are therefore present in the tissue fluid.

Analysing a graph

From the results obtained from an investigation into the digestion of protein in the presence of the enzyme trypsin, the graph shown below was drawn. The initial concentration of enzyme and substrate was the same at each temperature investigated. The pH of the medium was kept constant throughout.

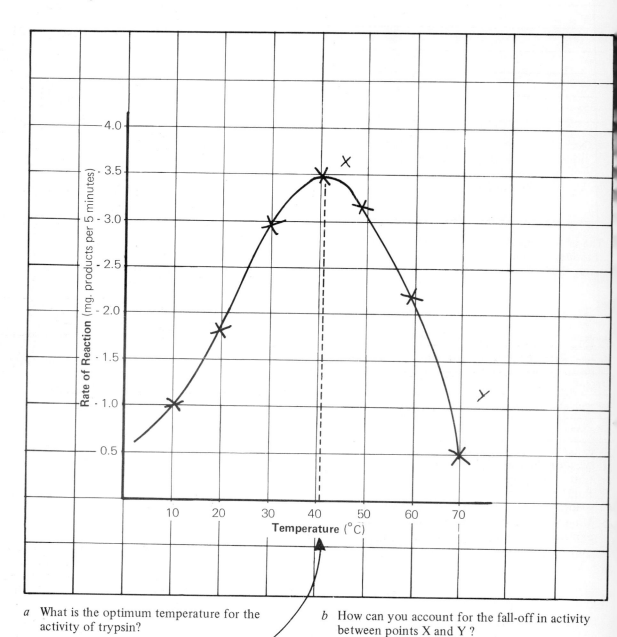

a   What is the optimum temperature for the activity of trypsin?

b   How can you account for the fall-off in activity between points X and Y ?

Answers

a   The optimum temperature for trypsin activity is 42°C.

b   At temperature above 42°C trypsin activity decreases. This may be because trypsin is a protein and when heated, proteins are denatured.

Labelling a dissection

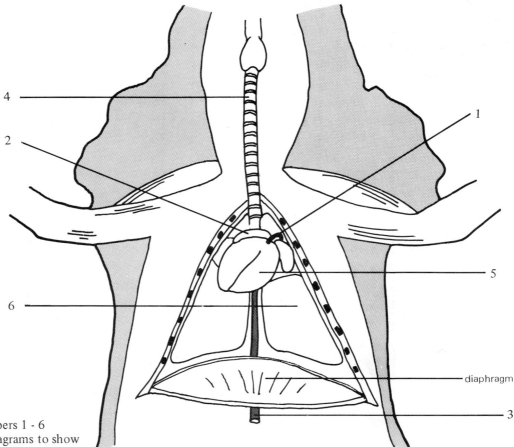

Dissection of thoracic region of rabbit

a Label the above diagram — numbers 1 - 6

b In the spaces below draw two diagrams to show the positions of the diaphragm and ribs when the animal

   i **inspires**   *ii* **expires**

c Which part of the heart receives blood from the lungs ? . . . .

Answers

a 1. pulmonary arch 2. right auricle or atrium 3. posterior or inferior vena cava 4. trachea 5. left ventricle 6. left lung.

b

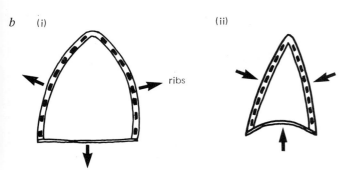

c left auricle/atrium

Notes

a The rabbit, like man, is a mammal and so the arrangement of organs and their functioning is similar. Labels etc. are the same as for man. Many syllabuses state that you should see a rabbit or rat dissected.

b There are alternative names for some organs all of which are acceptable e.g. right auricle = right atrium.

c You do not have to be an artist to draw diagrams. Simple sketches will do, especially if accompanied by accurate labels.

d The amount of space provided gives some indication of the detail required.

The essay type of question

1 Name two types of cell division

2 Give an example of where in the body each type of division may occur and describe the main differences between them.

NOTE: Essay-type answers are often clearer with relevant, fully-explained diagrams. These can form a large part of the answer especially where descriptions are asked for.

A Break question into sub sections. Deal with each sub section in order.

B Note main points for each sub section, omit points specifically excluded in the question. Note appropriate diagrams.

C Write up essay in minimal grammatical English, dealing with each sub section in order. Insert diagrams in exact place in text.

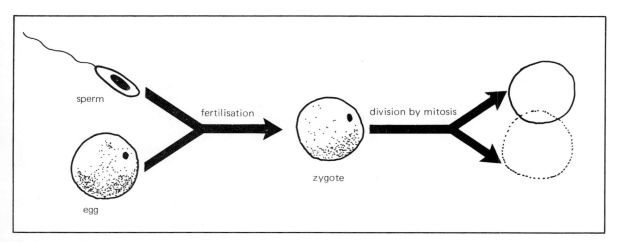

Answer

1 The two types of cell division are Mitosis and Meiosis
2 Mitosis occurs when the zygote, that is, the fertilised egg divides

Meiosis takes place in the testes of the man and results in the production of the sperms, and in the ovaries of the woman resulting in the production of the eggs or ova.

The nuclei of normal body cells, that is all cells apart from the gametes (sperm and ova) contain twenty three pairs of chromosomes. When a cell undergoes mitosis two new cells are produced that are genetically identical with each other and with the original dividing cell.

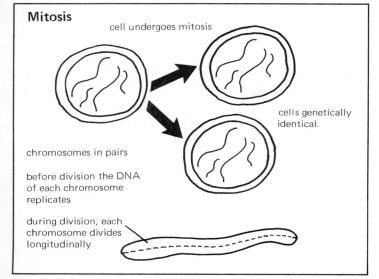

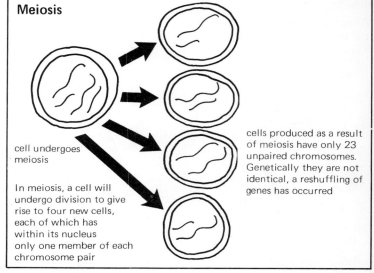

Index